Harold Carlton wa ed
Kilburn Grammar In
1988 he wrote a n on
copies in the USA His
next novel, *Sacrifi The
Scarf*, a history of me
between Pimlico, L e is
working on a new novel.

What the critics said:

' … bitterly funny … It is a brilliant portrait … comes alive through dialogue, which Carlton handles wonderfully. … This seems like a book that had to be written – as if its humiliations could be mastered only by putting them on the page. It is a remarkable achievement.'

John Carey, *The Sunday Times*

' … bitter-sweet memoir of life lived in and around Jewish Maida Vale featuring a gallery of colourful family personalities seen through the eye of an artistic young boy.'

Jewish Chronicle

'There are nicely observed bits of teenage business, often about sex, and the tone is bitter-sweet and sometimes comic … besides all this jokey stuff about grandmothers and *shiksas*, something more interesting emerges. The dramatic events and revelations towards the end change the whole tone of the book and put the earlier chapters in quite a different light. The picture darkens and Carlton makes some revealing points about post-war British Jewishness. … quiet, rich and full of interest.'

David Herman, *Jewish Chronicle*

'Raw, entertaining account of post-war Jewish family life.'
The Sunday Times

' … elegant and precise prose … Although the novel encompasses some gloomy themes – death, divorce, betrayal and rejection – it retains a charming delicacy. … Howard is a funny, likeable and self-effacing lad whose final summation, as he charts the ends of his characters, shows enviable wisdom.'

Toby Clements, *Daily Telegraph*

'The way in which the characters traverse social divides is a distinct feature of this work. I defy anyone not to recognize at least one person in the story. Carlton's work is refreshingly witty and real. ... The narrative trots along with dry, beautifully under-stated wit as the young Harold struggles to come to grips with the eccentricities of his immediate family. ... a compulsive and captivating read that will linger in the memory.'

Soho Independent

'A pleasure to read ... an unsentimental book, neither a whine nor a boast, about growing up in a difficult family.'

Salley Vickers

'The first sentence, a little masterpiece, shows the reader how good it is going to be. A wonderful mixture of sophistication and innocence, and how shrewd he is about a family. I did enjoy *The Handsomest Sons in the World* very much!'

John Bayley

'I loved *The Handsomest Sons in the World!* Very funny, sharp, without that cloying sentiment which mars so many memoirs. ... though so many scenes recalled approach a glorious kind of slap-stick comedy, there was always that bite of truth underneath. I laughed at so many bits ... and the ending has some real shocks.'

Margaret Forster

'You really must read *The Handsomest Sons in the World!*'

The Sunday Times

'Absolutely fascinating ... brilliant!'

Ned Sherrin, *Loose Ends*, BBC Radio Four

'Most enjoyable ... gracefully written ... a lovely funny-sad portrait of the grandmother.'

Gavin Lambert

' ... gripping, funny portrait of Jewish life in 1950s London.'

Caroline Gascoigne, *The Sunday Times*

The Handsomest Sons in the World!

The Handsomest Sons in the World!

Harold Carlton

Duckbacks

Published in 2002 in Duckbacks, a paperback
imprint of Duckworth Media Group

First published in 2001 by
Duckworth Literary Entertainments, Ltd.
61 Frith Street, London W1D 3JL
Tel: 020 7434 4242
Fax: 020 7434 4420
email:DuckEd@duckworth-publishers.co.uk
www.ducknet.co.uk

A CIP catalogue record for this book is available
from the British Library

ISBN 0 7156 3158 6

Typeset by Derek Doyle & Associates, Liverpool
Printed in Great Britain by
BOOKMARQUE Ltd, Croydon, Surrey

For two special ladies:

Valerie Forman, the first person to explain Judaism to me, was one of my most beloved and valued friends. She died in her hundredth year, in 1993.

Mary Lutyens, equally loved, encouraged my writing this book. I read aloud the first half to her. She died, aged ninety, in 1999, before I finished my work.

A few words ...

When it came to telling my tale, I found that I could only do so as 'Howard Conway' though he is, of course, me. Some other names were changed to protect my family's privacy.

A twelve-year-old's understanding of events is like a game of Chinese Whispers, complete with hearsay, rumours and misinterpretations. Perhaps more so in my secretive family, where many did not even know their real birthdates. I have stayed true to my childhood impressions, uncorrected by hindsight.

Acknowledgements

Jean Csaky is the most generous fellow-writer and friend. Her help and advice contributed enormously to this book. As did Joan Marquès'.

For their criticism and/or encouragement, my sincere thanks to:

Helen Aronson (dear cousin), Nicola Beauman, Lucy Berthoud, Catarina Estarellas, Patricia Leckie, Daphne Lera, Rabbi Julia Neuberger, Sam North, Amanda Pallant, Anna Pallant, Elizabeth Suter (Darling Su), Jill Gibbons Yadav, and, for her patient photocopying, Francisca Bibiloni Sastre.

Thank you to my editor Sarah Such. And lastly, but not at all least, my agent Jane Turnbull who is 'Simply the Best!'

CONTENTS

Monkey Puzzle Trees and Crazy Paving 1

My New Auntie 18

'My Son's Ashamed of Being a Jew!' 25

The *Simcha* 35

Getting the *Shiksa* out of his System 45

Enter Two Adoring Female Eccentrics 55

Bringing Art to the Family 67

The Brothers' Return 77

'Who Needs the Brothers?' 93

The Rift 100

Clearing Out the Factory 109

'Don't Leave Me!' 116

Keeping Mario Happy 123

Marital Aids 130

The Secret 142

A Snip, a Cut and an Extra Stitch 150

''E Didn't Invite 'Is Own Mother to the Wedding' 162

Ciao, Vito! 175

The Wedding 181

Death of a Father Figure 191

The End of my Childhood 204

GLOSSARY OF YIDDISH AND HEBREW WORDS

Bris: circumcision ceremony
Chuppah: wedding canopy
Chuzzerai: pig-food, rubbish
Gedempt: stewed
Grobbykop: muddlehead, idiot
Kiddush: prayer for the dead
Kneidlach: dumplings in soup
L'chayim: to Life! (A toast when drinking.)
Mazel: luck
Mazeltov: good luck
Meschuga: mad
Mischegas: madness
Minyan: minimum of ten men for religious service
Pisher: little pisser, someone of no account
Shabbos: the sabbath
Schkop: fat cow
Schlepp: drag, or pull
Schmerel: idiot
Shiksa: non-Jewish girl
Shul: synagogue
Simcha: family event like wedding or barmitzvah

1

Monkey Puzzle Trees and Crazy Paving

The rise and fall of my family took place between my twelfth and fifteenth years and it is a tribute to my self-absorption that I hardly noticed. At the age of twelve I believed that everyone's family was exactly like mine. I thought every boy had a beautiful mother who adored him and a bad-tempered father who frightened him. I thought that all children loved their mothers and hated their fathers, that all families toasted cheese on toast and called it Welsh Rabbit, slept with their bedroom doors wide open and windows tight shut, made tea by pouring boiling water through a tea-filled strainer, and filled bookshelves with china ornaments since there wasn't a book in the house.

We lived in the London suburb of Willesden, postal district NW10. Our large semi-detached home was reached after driving through Kensal Rise and up Chamberlayne Road into a Jewish enclave. Most front gardens boasted a tall Monkey Puzzle tree and were criss-crossed with crazy paving. Our back garden had flowering broom and lilac, plus cherry, pear, plum and apple trees from which we impatiently ate unripe fruit and got tummy-ache. I liked to sit reading in the lower, broad branches of the cherry tree, feeling as if I were daringly high in the sky.

My mother's cries of delight at my first doodles had convinced me that I must be an artist. She considered me a genius. It never crossed my mind that she might be biased. I was a trusting child and tended to believe what I was told. The problem was that a genius artist did not really fit the niche that my family had carved for itself.

Jews did not become artists, my parents explained. They became accountants, doctors or lawyers, or they went into their parents' businesses. Since my father manufactured ladies' handbags, this was not a very exciting prospect.

I had an elder sister, Rachel, who took me around with her if no one better showed up, and a younger brother, Lawrence, whose main aim in life was the destruction of all my possessions. Both my sister and my brother believed that I was the favourite. I was one of six Jewish boys in a grammar school of five hundred. The odd taunt of 'Dirty Jew' was hurled at me, but it was as automatic as red-haired boys getting 'Ginger' or acne-afflicted boys getting 'Spotty'.

'They're just jealous, darling,' Mum assured me, her all-purpose explanation of any hostile behaviour towards me. I wondered what they were jealous of.

I grew up pretty oblivious to any evil in the world. We were told that the Nazis had killed my father's parents, but later found out they hadn't. Perhaps it was my parents' clumsy way of alerting us to the fact that being Jewish often meant persecution.

I felt so different from my family that I sometimes wondered whether I had secretly been adopted. I often leafed through the family photograph album to study the first snaps of us arriving back from the nursing home, swaddled in white shawls in our mother's arms. Neatly pasted in beneath the photographs were clippings from *The Jewish Chronicle*'s Births announcements, which I reluctantly accepted as proof that I was a *bona fide* member of this family.

I knew that my mother adored me. She assured me that my father did too. But when my father loved someone it was a secret; someone else had to tell you. I did not really believe he loved any of us. My mother whispered to me that I was the light of her life, which I took to be a pretty responsible title, as if her happiness and well-being was up to me. I had been extremely dependent on her as a small child and remembered with shame my behaviour at the age of five or six, when I cried at the very idea of her leaving my presence. If she left the house I would feel sick and stand at her bedroom window for hours, awaiting the sight of her dear head bobbing up at the foot of our hill as she returned with heavy shopping. I was terribly ashamed of this and got over it by lying awake at night imagining her death and subsequent funeral. Picturing this almost unimaginable event, I would soak my pillow with tears, grieving before the tragedy in order to better prepare myself for it. Once I had got her death out of the way, I felt free to enjoy her company as 'extra' days spent with her.

At twelve, I was slowly reading my way through *The Collected Works of Sigmund Freud* in an attempt to gain insight into the way people – especially my family – behaved. I obtained the books from Willesden Library by informing the librarian that my Mum was ill and needed reading matter. Freud's work was on the Restricted list. 'Wouldn't she prefer a nice Agatha Christie?' the librarian asked, mildly surprised.

*

We were all frightened of my father because of his unpredictable temper. He was Polish and had come to London at the age of thirteen. He had the trace of an accent, which became more pronounced when he was in a rage. The rage was always there, lurking, and flared up over trivial things: orange squash spilt on the table cloth, a dropped fork. He would lash out at the nearest child, slapping face or head, or roar very suddenly at full blast in an ear, frightening us to tears. Rachel and I always tried to make sure that Lawrence was sitting nearest to him at the dining table. When Dad left the house in the mornings, it was as if a black cloud lifted from our lives. We would join hands and dance in a circle around the hall, singing. Perhaps my mother shouldn't have encouraged us, but the relief was too great. We loved knowing that she was on our side, celebrating the departure of the ogre for a full day at the handbag factory. Possibly she was afraid of him too?

My mother was Hollywood-beautiful with a heart-

shaped face, big sparkling brown eyes, a small straight nose
and a full mouth. I assumed that everyone's mother was
beautiful and was surprised when my friends' mothers
sometimes turned out to be dull or plain. Mum thought we
were perfect too, especially me, and she stuffed red ribbon
into my shoes when I was little to ward off the evil eye
from other mothers. She maintained that my only problem
in life would be coping with my unfairly good looks. This is
not borne out by contemporary photographs. I was a
pleasant-looking, plump child but hardly likely to provoke
such intense envy.

As much as I adored my mother and couldn't get
enough of her company, I hated my father and avoided his.
I felt guilty about both of them: needing and loving my
mother so much, hating my father so much. The fact that
my sister and brother hated Dad too made me feel a little
less guilty. Also, Dad had no friends – not one. That surely
proved something?

I once forgot to greet my father in the morning rush.

'Don't you say good morning to the dog?' he asked.

'Sorry, Dad,' I muttered.

'Well?'

'I –'

'Say, "Good morning, dog!" ' he roared.

Knowing that it was somehow sick, I obediently
parroted 'Good morning, dog.' He nodded, satisfied. I diagnosed a classic inferiority complex, sure that Freud would
agree.

Dad had had a difficult childhood and sometimes
described it, briefly and vaguely, to us. It was a sad story
that included hunger, punishment, an over-strict father, the
early death of his mother and a horrid new stepmother he
had never accepted. He told this tale omitting facts, place-
names, dates, so that in my mind it happened in a
Dickensian fairytale land, dark, rainy and cold. We
invented a lot of his wretched childhood for him. We
decided he had witnessed his family being shipped off to
concentration camps, as whenever we asked him about
them, he said that the Germans had killed them. Penniless

and starving, he had escaped to London at the age of thirteen, wearing shoes without shoe-laces or socks. Unable to speak English, he had wandered the cold, wet streets of East London for what seemed like days.

This was the story my father liked to tell. But as we grew up and spoke to relatives, we learned that his background had not been nearly so bleak. He had voluntarily left Poland years before the Nazi menace and had joined two elder brothers already established in London. He had never gone hungry or barefoot. Why did he need so much sympathy from us?

Dad had married into partnership with his father-in-law, who owned a handbag factory. My mother was seventeen when she was married off. We refused to consider the idea of an arranged marriage, which it probably had been. My grandparents had wanted a very pretty and thus potentially troublesome daughter off their hands and safely married to a decent Jewish man. In the face of my father's ill temper and black moods, we clung to the belief that underneath he truly loved our mother – it was just another well-kept secret. Children want their parents to be in love. We saw him treat her cruelly but chose to believe the fairytale.

My father's factory supplied department stores with 'superior ladies' handbags in genuine hide leather'. Although it must have provided a good enough income, he always behaved as if we were penniless. He went into a rage if lights were left on accidentally, or even if mustard was left on a plate. Scraping the mustard back into the jar, he would shout: 'This is how mustard-makers get rich! Not from what you eat but from what you leave on the plate!'

However, like most things in the family, these economies were contradictory, for he drove a huge American car, an emerald and chrome number which so embarrassed us that we begged him to drop us several streets from school so that none of our classmates would see it. We kept a small house in Cliftonville where we spent summers by the sea. At Christmas, we would visit the factory in Kentish Town where employees set up tables on the work-floor and hung the place with paperchains and mistletoe.

One Christmas, breathing in the intoxicating fumes of glue, we goggled at a worker grabbing a girl he'd been eyeing all year. The mistletoe was the excuse for kissing her. The man bent forward, the girl backward, their mouths pressed together. The kiss went on and on until the entire factory fell silent. When the couple broke apart, they were flushed and breathless. Everyone cheered. Rachel and I exchanged looks; we had never seen our parents kiss like that.

Wasn't everyone's family exactly like mine? A father I hated, a mother I loved so much I had had to mentally kill her off? A beautiful Mum who, between maids, enjoyed dressing in rags and cheekily telling visiting salesmen who asked if they could see the lady of the house: 'Oh, she's out!' She was delighted when the disguise worked but when she went to parties or dances, she looked more dazzling than any woman we had ever seen. And didn't everyone have a father whose slight foreign accent became more pronounced when he raged and who read nothing but the *Daily Express*, muttering the words under his breath?

I thought that books were only to be found in libraries and I stole my parents' library-cards so I could borrow twenty books a week. I was mortified when I saw shelves of books in other boys' houses. I took it upon myself to attempt to correct my father when he mispronounced a word or put a sentence back to front.

'So this is what happens when you educate your children?' he raged at my first correction. 'Suddenly they know better than you?' It was made very clear that I must never correct him again.

We were urged to try for the best schools and were given extra tuition by teachers brought home after school. I suffered agonies of embarrassment at maths or history teachers being served tea by my chatty mother. After tea we studied in the dining room, using the glass-topped table, with one bar of the wall-fire on to 'take the chill off'. I failed the posh schools' exams and did not convince the masters that I loved sport, as I had been coached to do. I ended up in the local grammar, although my father resented my education as much as if I had gone to Oxford.

Dad was good at making us feel guilty. He suffered painful ulcers in the stomach, caused by 'aggravation', which was a much-used word in our family, always pronounced with meaningful looks at us, as if we were responsible.

'Dad? Where are we going for our summer holiday this year?' I would ask hopefully, each spring.

He always answered with a snarl: 'Your whole life is a holiday!'

*

In 1954 I was one year away from my barmitzvah, my thirteenth birthday, the day a Jewish boy becomes a man. I felt so far from becoming a man that the prospect filled me with dread. When I thought too hard about it, I would vomit. I imagined hair sprouting on my cheeks and my voice deepening or cracking overnight. I looked up puberty and adolescence in my pocket dictionary, but did not quite understand all the implications.

I did know all I would be required to do for my barmitzvah. I would have to sing a portion of the Torah in Hebrew at our local synagogue before family, friends and congregation. We would invite fifty people to our house for lunch after the service, and the following evening we would host a dinner and a dance for five hundred at caterers' rooms in Willesden Green. How could I get out of it? I didn't believe in the Jewish religion – or in any other religion. My father told me that religion was a lot of baloney, even while insisting we attend Hebrew classes and synagogue four times a week. When auditioning for my school choir, I had sung in a piping treble,

> 'There is a green hill far away, outside the city wall
> Where our dear Lord was crucified, he died to
> save us all …'

As I had sung 'our Lord', I had expected a bolt of lightning to strike me dead, but it hadn't and I had happily joined the choir.

We'd been told by the sour-faced Miss Klausner in Hebrew classes that Adam and Eve had been the first people on earth. Yet the schools' radio programme *How Things Began* said that the first creatures on earth were apes. I decided to go above Miss Klausner's head and ask Rabbi Kaplan if it was possible that Adam and Eve had been apes. I'd caught him on a bad day. 'No!' he growled impatiently. 'They were fish.' In the following weeks I tried hard to picture two salmon strolling in the Garden of Eden, fig-leaves modestly tucked between fins. I think it was right then that I lost the last thin shreds of faith.

Rabbi Kaplan was always in a bad temper. A chain-smoker, he wore a B-movie gangster's hat and took deep drags on his cigarettes, distorting his mouth to eject the smoke quickly from one corner. It seemed an unsuitable addiction for a religious man. His teenage daughter, 'Honey' Kaplan, wandered in and out of our classes like a provocative apparition, everything we had believed Jewish girls not to be: blonde, blue-eyed and slim.

I decided to confess my lack of faith to my father. Perhaps he would welcome saving the cost of a barmitzvah and let me off. I hated the long Saturday mornings in the synagogue with him, hearing the older men droning on, bending their knees now and then, to bow in the direction of Israel. To me it was really the direction of the West End where I longed to be, squandering my pocket-money in HMV. Sneaking glances at my Kelton 21 watch, I got hungrier and hungrier for lunch. I could not follow the service; although Hebrew classes had taught us to read Hebrew aloud fluently, we did not understand a word of what we read.

I tackled Dad before dinner one Friday evening. I was frightened of his unpredictable rages but felt that it was worth a try. He was sitting in one of the drawing room's comfortable navy armchairs upholstered in a twined rope pattern, reading his *Daily Express*. He heard me out without taking his head from the newspaper.

'It *is* a lot of baloney,' he nodded when I had finished, 'but you must have a barmitzvah. It's expected of you. It's not just for you, it's for the family, our friends, our business contacts …'

'But I don't believe in it,' I cried.

Dad put aside the paper and looked at me. He was a handsome man, but I disliked everything about him. His voice with its slight Polish accent, his dark hair combed straight back flat against his head, his threatening, impatient manner.

'Just make us proud of you on that Saturday,' he tried. 'Sing your portion of the law well, make a nice speech at the dinner, and after that you never need to set foot in a synagogue again.'

I stared at him. 'Really?'

It was almost too good to be true. He had gone back on his promises before, but this was much too good a deal to turn down. One more year of baloney religion, one barmitzvah ceremony and then … goodbye God, goodbye Hebrew, goodbye prayers, synagogue, droning men and bowing in the direction of Israel?

'Okay!' I held out my hand to shake on it. Dad glanced at my hand.

'We don't need to shake hands, you can trust your father,' he said. I left the room, triumphant.

*

The high point of our week was Saturday afternoon tea at my grandparents' flat. They lived 'up West' in a long, dark mansion flat off the Edgware Road. They were very proud of their home and lived there all their lives, in spite of becoming accidentally, mythically, rich later. They were unable to imagine anywhere finer and for this alone I loved them. I loved them for not wanting more. Indeed they might have been more comfortable with less, for the furnishings, mirrors and chandeliers were considered so precious that not even their owners were able to enjoy them: they were perpetually shrouded first in thick transparent plastic, then in dust-sheets. Most rooms were too good to use or even see, especially the best room which was always firmly locked. The flat could be as glittering as a fairytale palace when all the chandeliers were switched on. The curtains were tightly drawn against the outside world in winter, and at evening meals we felt we had wandered into a pantomime, with Grandma playing both Fairy Godmother and Wicked Witch.

One Saturday, about a year before my barmitzvah, Grandpa opened the front door. A gentle, plump, cuddly man, he kissed us and led us down the long, dark corridor towards the kitchen. It was a kitchen unlike any other, lit by a ballroom-sized chandelier that filled the upper half of the room. Glossy white walls bounced back a dazzling light, blocked by a bulky figure who stood waiting for us, arms akimbo. She had already begun to scream and her voice rose in volume as we drew nearer: 'Oooooooohhhhhhheeeeeee!' The light splayed behind her as if a spotlight was trained on the back of her head, lighting up a mop of frizzy orange hair that was piled up in an untidy bunch, like a Toulouse Lautrec cancan dancer's. Her face was powdered dead white and her crimson mouth stretched in a welcoming smile so wide it became a grimace. She caught us up one by one in her arms.

''*Allo darlin'*!' She held me at arm's length, her eyes alive and sparkling, sometimes grey, sometimes green. 'Gimme a kiss!' she commanded. '*Mmmmwhhahhhh*!'

Several kisses, each a suction-pad of love, were plonked over my face. Thrusting me back to arm's length again she scrutinised me, staring into my very soul. How she loved us! Her eyes brimmed with tears, as if such love was too much to ask a human being to bear. As if love were tragic and God unreasonable to give her such adorable grandchildren. Briskly wiping away these tears, she plucked the next child from the corridor to begin all over again.

'Now we're all together!' she cried triumphantly. 'Soon we'll *eat*!'

Grandma never spoke in a normal voice – she was

either screaming or whispering family secrets *sotto voce*. She seemed to feel more than any other person. She cried more, she laughed more. We clustered around her, staring up at her, wondering what she would do or say next. Would she pinch our cheeks until they hurt? Throw a herring into our mouths? Suddenly go into a rage because we had said a word that she considered vulgar but wasn't vulgar at all? Would she say one of her invented words such as 'suffragettes' for Selfridges, 'wirelist' for wireless, or 'spoom' for spoon?

''Ow's your little cock-a-doodle-do?' Grandma growled in my ear, doubling up with laughter. It was one of the naughty words she was allowed to use, although God help us if we said something she thought was naughty, like 'rock and roll' which she misheard as 'Rotten Row' and thought obscene.

In the blindingly bright kitchen, aromas of smoked fish, cream cheese and olives were mixed with Grandpa's cigar smoke and Grandma's perfume. The kitchen light was cruel and we stared at Grandma's make-up, fascinated. If we were early, we might be lucky enough to catch her applying it at her bedroom dressing table, slapping her face just once with a powder-puff loaded with chalky white powder. She only ever hit her nose, which was always whiter than the rest of her face. She shut her eyes tightly so they emerged as two dark craters, like a silent movie star's. Her face always appeared to be lit from beneath, as if by Edwardian footlights. Two circles of rouge adorned her cheeks and her lips were always Revlon's Fire and Ice scarlet. Her long, blood-red nails were always protected by white cotton gloves.

We entered a different world in Grandma's flat, where people ate, spoke and dressed in surprising ways. Underwear played a large part in my grandparents' wardrobes; covered by a bathrobe or apron, Grandma favoured white satin slips over matching bloomers, Grandpa a sleeveless white vest. Their garments, whether outer or under, were always spotless, as if just donned from a pristine laundry delivery. Grandma was always in a flurry

of activity, frying fish for twenty guests or scrubbing down
kitchen walls from the top of a ladder, her Irish maid Mary
holding it steady for her, calling up: 'Be careful, Mrs G!'
Their real surname, unpronounceable, had been reduced
down to their initials: Mr and Mrs G.

Was Grandma ugly or beautiful? This was a hard one to
decide, however long we stared at her. She was an ugly
woman who believed she was beautiful and made us
believe it too. Children have an instinct for the false; if her
self-confidence had been less than genuine, we would have
ridiculed her. As it was, we swallowed her self-image
whole, fearing and loving her. She was of medium height,
squat and heavy. Her large nose was crowned with a big
brown mole. Her greenish eyes could sparkle with mischief
or turn grey with self-pity. She lived for her sons – 'the
handsomest sons in the world', as she never stopped telling
us. Jack, the younger, still lived at home and was only eight
years older than me. Frankie had mysteriously disappeared
to New York some years before and had married an
American woman: they had a small daughter. All I knew of
him were vague memories of playing with him and the
colour movies my grandparents brought back from their
visits to New York, their little granddaughter Barbara
waving from Fifth Avenue as yellow cabs flashed by
behind her.

There were so many things to do at Grandma's that we
always went a little mad there. We might be allowed to rifle
through the drawers of the sideboard where we would find
New York matchbooks, *Folies Bergères* programmes with
photographs of naked women, aromatic cigar-boxes
stuffed with mah-jong pieces, casino chips, dice, receipts,
playing cards and old postcards. We could race down the
corridors, trying all the locked doors to see if one was
open, like burglars casing a joint.

Once we pushed open the door of the 'best' room and
flicked on the light. A blast of icy air rushed out at us as we
peered at the armchairs and sofas draped in white sheets.
The thousands of tiny mirrored squares on the cocktail
cabinets reflected the lights of the triple-tier chandelier

above. The room sparkled like a snow-filled paperweight and we felt as privileged as visitors to a Versailles pavilion opened exclusively for us. The dining room held a long mahogany table with fourteen chairs, their backs and seats covered in burgundy brocade, and the largest television-radiogram console anyone had ever seen.

'Children!' A scream issued from the kitchen. 'We're going to eat!'

We raced to the kitchen where grease-proofed paper packages from the fridge were piled in the centre of the Formica-topped table. Grandma served food in its original packaging, which we found exciting – like eating in a grocery shop. At home, cheese or ham slices were genteelly fanned out on a platter. Spilling from the packages, mixing their savoury smells, were smoked salmon, new green pickled cucumbers, bitter black shiny olives and chopped herring. A small bowl of cream cheese, lightly soured, nudged a pile of pink oblong ham slices. The ham was incongruous amongst all the Jewish deli food – it wasn't kosher but it tasted better because of that. Our tea was a kind of picnic on the kitchen table.

Grandpa carved chunks of yellow *challah* and a big slab of white, unsalted Danish butter began to melt in its saucer. We stared at this feast, almost fainting with sudden hunger. For the children there was a big glass jug of Kia Ora pineapple-orange squash. The central heating was so strong that we were always thirsty and dreaded the jug emptying because it never got filled up again. Grandma made tea for the grown-ups. Teapots were unknown in our family. Boiling water was poured from the kettle through a strainer holding fresh tea leaves, straight into the cup.

My family shared the Chinese view that a fat child was a healthy child. I thought meals were supposed to end in pain – the stretched tight feeling of an overstuffed stomach. The greatest compliment one could give to the cook, in our family, was to gasp, clutch one's tummy and head for a bed.

Halfway through tea, Uncle Jack stumbled in from his bed.

'You've slept for seventeen hours,' Grandma cried approvingly as he stood there, face stubbly, hair sticking out, in his crumpled white undervest and shorts.

We stared at our uncle. It was difficult to believe that anyone as ancient as Grandma could have such a young son. 'What are you doing this evening?' she asked him as he poured himself some tea.

'Dunno.' Jack replaced the kettle and came to sit beside us. 'Go to the pictures, maybe?'

'On yer *own*?' Grandma screamed. ''Andsome young man like you? On 'is own on a Saturday *night*?' Jack sipped his tea, staring at his mother over the rim of his cup with mournful black eyes. 'Make some *friends*,' Grandma advised, as she did each Saturday. 'Find a nice *boy* to go around with. I'll ask Mrs Bresslaw if 'er son would like a friend.'

'Don't, Ma,' said Jack warningly.

'Do me a favour,' she sighed. 'Moochin' around by yerself on a Saturday night. 'Andsome boy like you.' She dug me in the ribs. 'Isn't your uncle 'andsome?' she asked me. ''E oughta be in pictures 'isself!'

We stared up at our uncle. I didn't think him at all handsome. His sad black eyes were expressionless and he had inherited his mother's nose, complete with its large mole. Why wasn't Grandma saying how beautiful my mother was? The answer to that was quite simple: we had decided long ago that she was jealous of Mum, jealous of her own daughter. Mum had inherited her father's small, straight nose and his kindly nature. It was no secret that she was Grandpa's favourite. In retaliation, Grandma had made the boys her favourites and did her best to ignore my mother or put her down.

She grabbed Jack by the neck to plant a noisy kiss on his forehead and then abruptly pushed her plate away.

'I'm *bursting*,' she gasped, fanning herself with a napkin.

This was our cue to say that we had had enough too, even if we hadn't. As the last slices of salmon, cheese and ham began to curl in the heat, we protested that we couldn't eat another bite and the paper packages were neatly refolded and put back in the fridge. Grandma lit a cigarette, followed by my mother, then my uncle. We watched the blue smoke from three Players curl up into the air.

'I've 'ad my manicure,' Grandma announced, peeling off her cotton gloves to reveal white, blue-veined hands with blood-red talons. She turned her hands this way and that as if she were in love with them. The strong curved nails were long and glossy. 'The woman said she'd never *seen* such nails,' she said contentedly, replacing the gloves. ' "Of course not," I told 'er. " 'Ow many women do you know 'oo wear gloves all the time?" '

The manicure would have taken place in her bedroom, probably; Grandma and Grandpa had a small army of devoted women who arrived at their flat to perform various tasks on hands, feet, backs, upper lips and heads: styling hair, removing hair, massaging. It was another thing that made them different, almost royal.

Grandma launched into her after-tea monologue. It always centred on how other people wasted their money, ruined their children, asked for trouble, requested her advice then ignored it. She loved criticising and she was merciless. She only broadcast bad news and misfortunes. My parents either laughed or agreed with her. Grandpa listened in silence, making it obvious that he had heard the monologue before, probably several times. She fed him lines:

'Didn't I, Max? ... Wasn't it just like that, Max? ... Am I making this up? ... Am I right or am I wrong?'

And Grandpa would grunt, 'You're right,' or 'Sure!'

I listened, a little fearful. I never wanted to be in Grandma's bad books. She seemed able to curse people, if only through her withering laugh. If anyone had had a success or was happy, she'd give a 'harrumph' as if to indicate that it couldn't last.

Finally the grown-ups would begin to talk business or discuss new ways to make a better living, or even a fortune. This was known as scheming and it could go on for hours. We would escape to the room with the television, leaving them to it.

My grandparents never kissed or touched, not even a hand on a shoulder in passing. I took it for granted that they had a perfect marriage. They must have, because they were my grandparents.

*

Some Saturday afternoons Grandpa took me to the pictures. I met him around two o'clock, when he was finished at the barber's. Grandpa was a barbershop kind of guy, a customer who liked all the trimmings – scalp massage, cologne, hot towels – a good raconteur and a generous tipper. He was made very welcome by his barber, Lou, who was about the same age and girth as Grandpa. Lou treated Grandpa's nearly-bald pate as lovingly as if it were a baby, stroking, anointing, rubbing and finally powdering, so that when it was all over, Grandpa would walk up Edgware Road feeling like a million dollars, a fresh cigar between his lips.

We would pass a shop where a man working in the window spun glass into delicate swans, giraffes or unicorns. If I was lucky, Grandpa bought me one for my collection. Then we went to the Blue Hall, a flea-pit of a cinema where double bills of old movies were shown, the projection so rickety that the sound-track sometimes skipped entire phrases, rendering the plot meaningless. If the film was a musical, it was impossible to tap your feet to the rhythm. The rows of velvet-covered seats, as worn and soft as moss, had gaps like an old man's toothless grin. Plenty of patrons snoozed away an afternoon there, snoring until someone nudged them awake.

I enjoyed Grandpa's company so much. I loved his easy-going manner and his stories of his Paris youth, working in the Paris Opera. I imagined he had been a famous tenor. He knew all the arias and often burst into song – sometimes on the street – with his favourite from *I Pagliacci*: 'Ridi, Pagliaccio …'. He told me the story of the sad clown, forced to laugh in the face of tragedy. Although he was so keen on this sad clown, there was nothing sad about him.

He seemed to me an entirely contented man. My curiosity about him began one afternoon during a cinema visit, when he suggested we go to see Aunt Hilda, an aunt I hadn't even known I had.

2

My New Auntie

'We'll pop up to see Auntie Hilda,' Grandpa leaned over to announce in the flea-pit. It was only a scratchy old black-and-white Western, so I didn't mind.

'Okay,' I agreed.

Outside I took his hand and swung it as we walked. That's how simple life was for a twelve-year-old. No questions, no wondering who this new aunt was and why I had never heard of her. If Grandpa said we were visiting Aunt Hilda, Aunt Hilda it was. He leaned nearer as we walked.

'Don't say anything to Grandma.' He waited a moment before adding, 'They don't get on.'

I nodded, shooting him a look. I could well imagine that Grandma didn't get on with anyone Grandpa might like. We turned into a small street off the Edgware Road, parallel to his own street, but a few blocks apart. It seemed perfectly normal that Aunt Hilda should live here, even rather convenient. It would never have occurred to me that there was anything odd or hidden about it. Grandpa was ancient. If anyone had told me that sixty-year-olds had sex, I would have been incredulous. Sex was a mysterious thing that newly-weds did to have babies. That ruled out Grandpa. He was a pleasant-faced, cuddly man and always smelled of barbershop cologne, but I would never have seen him as sexually desirable.

Stopping at a green door, he rang a bell and pushed open the door to peer up a steep flight of stairs. A woman appeared at the top.

'It's me, Hilda!' Grandpa called up. 'With my grandson.'

'Ooooh, lovely!' came a cry. 'Come up, then.'

The woman who hugged me at the top of the stairs felt fresh and vital. She had dark eyes gleaming from behind narrow spectacles. Her neat black hair was pulled back tightly into a bun and her smiling lips were bright red. She kissed Grandpa on the cheek and ushered us into her tidy flat.

'So this is your grandson.' She peered at me. 'What's your name, dear? And how old are you?'

'Howard. I'm twelve.'

'Twelve? Well, that's lovely, Howard! Quite a grown-up young man. Been to the pictures with your Grandpa, have you? Good film?' She bustled about and I noticed that the round table, covered with a crisp white cloth, was set for three, as if she had been expecting us.

'I told you not to go to any trouble,' Grandpa said, glancing at the plate of buttered malt-bread slices, the scones and the biscuits.

'Oh, what trouble?' Hilda laughed, fetching the kettle. 'A few slices of bread? You'll want something with your tea.'

The flat was conventionally furnished, on the modest side, almost shabby but well scrubbed. It was heated by a couple of wall-mounted electric bars. The patterned rug did not quite reach the walls and linoleum in a different pattern filled in the rest. A brown-tiled mantelpiece held a clock, some knick-knacks and a vase of drooping red tulips. Hilda obviously liked china ornaments, and she displayed each on its own white doily. She brought a small Dundee cake to the table and a teapot under a knitted cosy. I stared at the teapot, the first I had seen in a relative's home. I liked Hilda's vitality and the brusque no-nonsense way she served the tea. There was a trace of a Northern accent in her voice.

'Let's all sit down,' she suggested.

'He'll be eating another tea at his grandmother's,' Grandpa cautioned.

I saw a quick flash of hurt cross Hilda's face. 'Of course,' she nodded quickly. 'He won't want to spoil his appetite. Well,' she frowned, 'just try a bit of cake, then, dear, and half a cup of tea. All right?'

'Oh, I can easily manage two teas,' I assured her. She gave a wide smile.

'That's all right, then,' she said, pouring me a full cup. She poured tea for Grandpa. 'And can *you* eat two teas, Mr G?' she asked mischievously. 'Go on.' She offered the plate of buttered malt-bread. 'Do you good to have a tuck-in.'

I bit into the bread, staring at her. 'Do you work in the handbag factory?' I asked her.

She gave a peal of laughter, darting a look at Grandpa. 'Oh no, dear, I run a Lyon's teashop. I'm manageress of the Marble Arch branch. You ought to bring him in, Max.'

I noted that she called Grandpa 'Max'.

'What do you want to be when you grow up, Howard?' she asked.

'An artist,' I said importantly.

'What are you talking about?' Grandpa's mood changed instantly. He frowned at me. 'Don't be ridiculous.' He looked over at Hilda. 'He'll come into the factory,' he explained. 'Take it over. I've run it long enough.'

'Lovely,' said Hilda, nodding in approval. 'Try some cake?'

My mouthful of cake stuck in my throat. Take over the factory? No one had said anything to me about that, not even my mother. I quickly swallowed some too-hot tea.

'We've had ever such a busy week,' Hilda was saying. 'So many tourists in town. They come with all their shopping and they all want fish and chips. I suppose people think they're typically English.'

I let her chat on, stealing a glance now and then at Grandpa. He seemed unaware of the bombshell he had dropped into my brain. I seethed. I had never before announced my intention of becoming an artist and had expected encouragement. Hilda poured us more tea, stronger this time around. We sipped in silence.

'We'd better go soon,' Grandpa said. 'His brother and sister will be waiting at the flat, and his parents.'

'Of course.' Hilda nodded. She seemed fond of Grandpa and very respectful. 'How's Mrs G?' she asked. 'All right, is she? You will come back soon to see me, won't you, dear?' she said to me.

She gave me a brisk hug as I thanked her for the tea. Then she helped Grandpa on with his coat. Out on the dark landing, she held the front door wide open to give us some light.

'Sorry, the bulb's gone,' she said, glancing up. 'Be careful on the stairs. Howard? Perhaps you'd better go first.' I went ahead of Grandpa down the steep flight. I could hear him panting rather noisily behind me.

'Bye!' Hilda was calling. 'Bye, dear!' I reached the bottom and opened the front door. I heard Hilda's door close and Grandpa stumble. When I turned, he was sitting on the bottom stair, looking rather surprised.

'Grandpa!' I ran back. 'Are you all right? Should I call Auntie Hilda?'

He shook his head, holding up a hand. I tried to haul him to his feet. It wasn't easy, he was extremely heavy. I took a step back for extra leverage and pulled at his wrists with all my twelve-year-old force. He was breathless and a little wobbly when he finally got to his feet, his weight leaning on me like an entire building.

'I'll be all right,' he said. 'I'm fine. Just give me a few moments, get my breath.'

We stood in the entry, listening to the footsteps and chatter of people passing by outside. His heavy breathing grew calmer and we left. 'Don't tell your grandmother,' Grandpa reminded me urgently as we walked slowly towards his flat. 'She doesn't need to know.'

'About Aunt Hilda or you slipping?' I said.

'Both,' he said darkly. 'Tell her we saw the film round again.'

I glanced sideways at him, willing him back to his normal self. The idea of my big, solid grandfather being so vulnerable was terrifying. It meant that none of us was safe.

'Maybe you should call the doctor?' I suggested, when he leaned against the Marks and Spencer window for a few seconds.

'Who? That quack Kossoff?' he grunted. 'No, I'm just catching my breath, that's all.'

We started walking again, slower than we had ever walked. I felt that if I hadn't been at his side, supporting what felt like half his weight, he would just stop or collapse. How could he still be breathless after a little stumble, I wondered.

'I just need a sit-down,' he kept saying.

We finally reached Grandpa's dark street and the entrance to the flat. Only when he had dragged himself up the flight of carpeted stairs to the front door did he take a deep breath and appear to compose himself. As he turned his key in the lock, my grandmother's anguished cry – a kind of war-cry of worry – greeted us.

'My *God*, where 'ave you *been*?' She came hurtling down the corridor towards us, eyes wide and staring. 'I was worried out of my mind. I thought there must've been a' accident. I thought the cinema must've caught fire, or a bus driven onto the pavement. You can't imagine the things I've been picturing.'

For a moment I saw Grandma's Boschian view of a Saturday afternoon street and all the threats it held.

Grandpa glanced at his watch. 'We're only fifteen minutes late,' he said.

'Fifteen minutes? More like 'alf an hour!' Grandma snapped. 'What *'appened*?'

'We saw a bit of the film round again,' Grandpa said.

'You *what*?' Grandma peered suspiciously at us, clutching her heart. 'You took ten years off my life,' she complained, leading us to the kitchen. 'We've been waitin' and waitin'. I thought there'd been a' accident.'

My parents and my brother and sister were sitting around the table in the kitchen, beneath the glare of the chandelier, looking bored.

'Hello, darling.' My mother smiled at me. My sister rolled her eyes. Uncle Jack, awoken by the screams, wandered in from his bedroom in a white vest and shorts, scratching his head.

'What's wrong?'

'Nothin'!' Grandma said. 'Your father's just trying to give me a' 'eart attack, that's all.' Grandpa and I stood blinking in the bright light. 'Sit down, then, what's wrong with you?' Grandma practically pushed Grandpa into a chair.

'All this fuss,' he said. 'Just because we wanted to see a bit of the film again.'

Grandma rattled the kettle on the stove, making water spill and hiss.

'You didn't want to see a bit of no more film,' she said darkly, her back to us. 'Something 'appened! You think I can't tell? You 'ad a funny turn, *that's* what 'appened.' The kitchen went silent. Grandma spun around to face us. Everyone stared at Grandpa.

'I did not have a funny turn,' he said calmly. He shot me a quick look. 'But if you stop yelling for a moment, I'll tell you what happened.'

'Oh my God, *what*?' Grandma cried. 'What 'appened, Max? *Tell* me!'

Grandpa shook his head to himself, as if already regretting his admission. Grandma ran to him, bending down to feel his knees, his thighs, as if he were concealing some broken limb.

'Nothing happened,' Grandpa insisted. 'I slipped, okay? I almost fell over. That's what happened.'

Grandma stared into his face. 'Is that the truth?' she demanded. 'You *slipped*?'

Grandpa nodded. 'Ask Howard,' he said. All eyes turned to me.

'*Well*?' Grandma glared at me as if I had pushed Grandpa.

'Grandpa slipped,' I confirmed. 'Outside Marks and Spencer's.'

'Oh my *God*!' Grandma cried. 'What did you slip on?'

Grandpa shrugged. 'Who knows? A piece of fruit? Some dog dirt? You know how crowded Edgware Road is on Saturdays.'

'Outside Marks and Spencer's!' Grandma cried, shaking her head. 'So *near*! My God, so *near*!'

Grandpa stared at her. 'It's worse if it's near?' he said. 'If I'd slipped in Bournemouth, it wouldn't be so bad?'

Grandma gave him a withering look and returned to the stove.

'Your own 'usband can drop dead a few yards from yer own 'ome and you wouldn't even know,' she marvelled, tears brimming in her eyes. She brought two cups of tea to the table and dabbed her eyes.

'No one dropped dead, Mum,' my mother pointed out. 'Dad only slipped. People slip all the time. He's lucky he was with Howard.'

Grandma turned to me. 'And you didn't send for me?' she asked.

'We were on our way home,' Grandpa said.

Grandma leaned her weight on the edge of the sink and addressed us. 'Where were you *exactly*?' she asked.

'I told you! Outside Marks and Spencer's,' Grandpa replied. He sipped his tea.

'Oh my *God*! So *near*!' Grandma cried.

Rachel and I exchanged glances. We would be hearing variations on this theme for the rest of the evening. Grandma could be like a jazz musician improvising on a few notes, getting infinite variety out of them. I sipped my tea quietly. I had seen Grandpa lie, which was a shock. I hadn't realised anyone in my family could lie. I had also heard Grandpa tell Hilda that I was going to take over the factory. Should I bring this up with my parents, or pretend I hadn't heard? Why had I blurted out my intention to become an artist? Wouldn't it have been better to wait until I was twenty-one, then escape to Paris?

Grandma peered suspiciously at my plate. I had not immediately wolfed down the smoked salmon and *challah* placed on it.

'Did you *eat* something after the pictures?' she asked. I ate quickly; she did not miss the tiniest detail.

I kept quiet on the drive home that night, as my mother discussed Grandpa's funny turn in hushed tones. I felt incredibly grown-up because I had been trusted to keep Grandpa's secret.

3

'My Son's Ashamed of Being a Jew!'

Our household was run in a slightly more formal way than my grandparents' flat. No one walked around in their underwear and no one dreamed of staying in bed until five o'clock. In fact, going to bed was more of a punishment than a treat. My parents employed an Irish maid, a red-haired, tempestuous girl, named Sheila Toomey. She had a habit of studying herself in wall-mirrors for long moments before suddenly spitting at her reflection, crying, 'I *hate* you, Sheila Toomey!' We thought this was wonderful and took it in turns to spit at our reflections, crying, 'I *hate* you, Sheila Toomey!' The mirrors in our house were very clean after all this spitting. At weekends, lunch was served in the dining room, where the walnut and beige leather couch and armchairs were icy-cold in winter, cooling in summer. On a hot day, it was delicious to plop yourself down on the bouffant cushions and feel them slowly deflate under your weight. Lunch was served very slowly, the food saltless and tasteless. We called it 'ulcer food' because we all shared my father's bland diet that the doctor had advised. Nothing spicy or fried. My sister and I would exchange resigned glances, dreaming of our daring Chinese dinners in a Piccadilly Circus restaurant to which she sometimes took me. We once persuaded my mother, very much against her will, to try Chinese food with us there. She took the tiniest bite of plain boiled rice before clamping her hand over her mouth, running from the restaurant, hailing a taxi and vomiting the moment she reached home.

'Thank goodness she didn't try the Prawn Chop Suey,' my sister sighed.

Fizzy lemonade, delivered to the house in heavy glass siphons, was rationed out amongst us as carefully as water amongst lifeboat survivors. When the lemonade ran out, Kia Ora was poured from a tall pitcher. When that ran out, my father would say: 'If you're thirsty, drink water.' We felt very hard done by, imagining all the other boys and girls in the world drinking as much fizzy lemonade as they craved.

My father liked to compare our 'easy' lives to his hard one. We did not consider our lives at all easy. We saw ourselves chained to a treadmill of labour – working hard at school, studying at home with various private tutors, completing homework, practising the piano, attending Hebrew classes, preparing Sunday breakfast for our parents, washing the car on Sunday afternoons; we felt exploited.

My father's mood before Saturday lunch would determine whether or not our meal was going to be enjoyable. If he had collected few handbag repairs from the department stores that morning, he might be pleasant. Repairs to bags were the bane of his life; he considered them a terrible waste, both of profits and of his Saturday mornings, but he was obliged to accept them. More than a dozen snapped clasps or handles meant that anything might send him into a fury – overcooked food, food not cooked enough, spillages or giggling. He always thought we were laughing at him. Any mistake could trigger a roar, a cuff around the head or a hard slap.

Lunch began with a small liqueur-glass of advocaat with a splash of ruby-coloured cherry brandy floating in the centre. We sipped at this ambrosia slowly, savouring every sweet sticky drop, waiting for the burning in the throat and the slight giddiness that followed. The atmosphere would be nervy, tense, taut as a tightrope along which we inched our way: would one of us fall? Would someone drop a fork to the parquet floor or drip orange squash on the pristine white table cloth? Invariably my brother did, and my father would explode.

'Idiot! *Schmerel*! *Grobbykop*!' he would shout, slapping him. We only heard Yiddish words when he was angry. 'Why can't you be like your brother?' he would roar.

Lawrence would shoot me a look of pure hatred, his cheeks flaming, his eyes tear-filled and about to spill over. I would sit there, pleased and smug that it was not me. My mother would remonstrate with my father, making him angrier.

'Why can't you be more like your brother?' he would cry again. Freud himself could not have come up with a suggestion more certain to ruin brotherly love.

Freud got me through my last years of childhood. I gobbled up the case-histories, convinced I understood them. I read everything I could find about adolescence to see what lay in wait for me, and because I was worried that mine was late. The theories on infant sexuality were dense and exciting, but I could not really tie them in to my childhood. Once, by accident, I saw my mother naked. It was a shameful shock, as if I had been thrust face-to-face with her sexuality, her flaccid breasts a testament to her having borne three children, one of them me. Each week, I was obliged to scrub my father's back in his steamy bath. The sight of his hairy body, as repulsive to me as a spider, terrified me. I would close my eyes when he stepped out of the bath into the towel I held up for him. I filed neither of these experiences with naked parents under the heading of Sex. At twelve, I was pretty innocent but curious enough to peer into the windows of Marital Aids shops, examining the pink rubber bulbs and tubes, which I vaguely assumed were for enemas, never having undergone one. I wondered just how an enema could aid a marriage. With the same baffled curiosity, I watched the demonstrations behind the cycle-sheds at school given by the more developed boys. They would pull solemnly at themselves for long, boring minutes until a stream of white stuff erupted. It did not look like much fun, but I knew that until I could do it, I was far from manhood, whatever the Jewish religion said about becoming a man at the stroke of midnight on my thirteenth birthday.

As the barmitzvah crept closer, plans were drawn up, giving me twinges of fear each time they were mentioned. After Christmas, catering-rooms were visited, menus considered, bands auditioned and florists asked for centre-piece prices. It was going to be as big and as expensive as a wedding. I longed to be a teenager but I was not looking forward to the six months of studying beforehand, cooped up for hours in a back room of the synagogue with the chain-smoking Rabbi Kaplan. I thought it must be worth one further try to get out of the nightmare.

Dad was sitting in the armchair with his *Daily Express*, muttering the words under his breath. He muttered so quickly that I got the impression he didn't really understand what he was reading, much the same way I didn't understand the Hebrew I could read so fluently.

'Dad?' I asked from the doorway. 'Can I ask you something?'

'What?' He didn't lower his paper. I took a few steps towards him.

'Dad … I don't *feel* Jewish.'

'So? You think I do?'

'When I asked you about religion once, you said it was baloney.'

'It *is* baloney.'

'My teachers at Hebrew classes keep saying the Jews are the chosen people. What were we chosen for?'

He shrugged. 'Maybe it was to do what our parents tell us?'

I took a deep breath. 'This barmitzvah's going to cost a lot of money, isn't it? Should we really be spending all that on something no one really believes in?'

Now he lowered the paper to stare at me. 'First of all, *we're* not spending the money, *I'm* spending it,' he said. 'Second, you'll have a barmitzvah like every boy has a barmitzvah. You should be grateful we're giving you one.'

'But is that the reason?' I persisted. 'Are we going through all this just because everyone else does it? If they all stuck their hands in the fire, would we do it too?' This was the argument he used when we said 'Everyone does it.'

He raised his paper. 'Just make a good job of it,' he said. 'Your job is to make us proud of you. We're Jews and Jews get barmitzvah-ed.'

'Jews?' I cried. 'We never fast on *Yom Kippur*, we drive on Saturdays, we eat bacon and ham, we –'

'We're still Jews,' he said.

'But isn't it hypocritical to –'

'Now that's enough!' my father roared.

He lowered the paper with an angry rustle and gave me a long stare. I slunk off. At least I had had a good last try. It took until the following Saturday, as we all finished tea at my grandparents' flat, for my father to react.

'I'm *bursting*,' Grandma gasped, pushing her plate from her.

We all stopped eating. She peeled off her gloves to light a Players cigarette, her ruby nails gleaming. The chandelier blazed above and the last slices of salmon, cheese and ham began to curl in the heat. More Players were lit. And suddenly an animal-like cry burst out of my father. We all turned to his anguished face. I thought he must be choking on a piece of food. Then I realised that he was staring accusingly at me. Slowly, his hand lifted, his finger pointing.

'My son's ashamed of being a Jew!' he cried, his voice breaking. 'He doesn't want a barmitzvah!'

The table froze. Eyes swivelled, horrified, towards me. Inwardly, I groaned. This was my reward for trying to be honest with Dad. I felt a rush of heat to my face. I wanted to deny the charge but no words came. I stared back at him, trying to think of what to say.

'I'm not listening to this!' my sister cried.

She jumped to her feet and took off. We heard her running down the corridor and the slam of the front door. This in itself was unheard of; no one ever left Grandma's flat without kissing everyone goodbye. I admired Rachel's pluck and wished I could run after her. My grandparents made clucking noises. My mother stared at her plate. She could be strangely absent at moments like these, much as I willed her help.

'He doesn't want his barmitzvah. He's ashamed of being a Jew!' my father cried again.

After an eternity, I managed to moisten my lips and reply: 'I am not ashamed.'

'Are you *proud* of being a Jew?' Dad shot back.

What was there to be proud of, I wondered. What have you ever given me to be proud of? I didn't dare say it.

'Yes,' I said weakly, hating myself.

He knew very well that I was neither proud nor ashamed. It would have been like being proud to have brown hair. My grandparents exchanged a look. Can't you see how deranged he is? I prayed to them. Can you see now how horrible he makes our lives? He was usually so quiet and mild with them, saving the rages for us.

'Of *course* you'll 'ave a barmitzvah, darlin',' Grandma said soothingly. 'Every boy 'as a barmitzvah. It'll be lovely, cousins comin' from all over the world. You'll get plenty of presents! And your grandfather and I will be givin' you ...' she paused importantly, taking a puff of her cigarette, '... two 'undred pounds!'

There was a collective gasp. It was a colossal amount. Far too much for merely attaining thirteen years.

'That's what we give our first grandson,' Grandma said, nodding.

'Say thank you to your grandparents,' my father muttered.

'Thank you, Grandma and Grandpa,' I obeyed.

Clever of her, I thought, to save the day with a promise of money. She knew how to mollify my father, knew that for him there wasn't a thing in the world you couldn't settle with money. But the money would mean nothing to me. I wouldn't be allowed to spend it, I knew. It would be saved somewhere until it crumbled and dried out like the old liqueur chocolates Grandma saved for special occasions. How many boxes of those had we opened to find nothing but brittle shells?

The evening took up from where it had been interrupted. Uncle Jack wandered in in his underwear, unaware that anything had happened. They discussed which California-based cousins would make the trip. No one mentioned my sister or the fact that she might be wandering the streets. I tried to enjoy the return to normality, but I was already resolving never again to confide in my father. Unable to communicate with me, he had saved it up to explode to my grandparents, twisting my words. I had never said I was ashamed of being Jewish. I suddenly realised he was the one ashamed, not me. A classic case of what Freud would call 'projection'.

Back home, we found Rachel in her room, playing Elvis Presley records as if nothing had happened. No one asked her how she had got home. So typical of our family, I thought, glancing in at her bedroom and watching her jive with the wardrobe doorknob, using it as if it were a man's hand to propel herself into petticoated spins. Nothing would be said. The accusation, Dad's voice cracking like an animal's cry – it would all be glossed over.

'You like this screaming?'

With a start, I realised that Dad had crept up behind me. He frowned at the music and waited until Rachel turned it down. In my room, choosing a book to escape into, I found myself hating him with a new force that scared me. It couldn't be healthy for someone to hate his father this much.

'Bloody Pole,' I muttered to myself.

My brother heard. 'Yeah,' he giggled. 'Bloody Pole!'

Freud did not write much about being Jewish. If he did, it was not in his *Collected Works*. When I visited his last dwelling in Hampstead, years later, his artefacts and statuette collection showed more of an interest in Egyptology than in Judaism, or perhaps they overlapped. If I couldn't believe in God, I would believe in Freud. He had the stern, intelligent face of a god, he knew what life was about and he did not expect you to pray to him or worship him or to forgo delicious foods like bacon and shrimp. I did not understand all I read about repressed memories, the Oedipus complex, incest or paedophilia, but I kept doggedly reading. I learned that hostility between father and son was sometimes caused by the close relationship between mother and son, so close that the father became jealous. This made sense. I *was* closer to my mother. In some ancient societies, I read, there had been a fight (to the death!) between strong young son and aging father.

The father was fighting to retain his power. Was this what was happening between my father and me?

*

Study sessions for the barmitzvah began with Rabbi Kaplan. Three times a week he sang the phrases from the Torah portion I was to recite and I echoed them in my piping treble, which was still very much a treble with no hint of a maturing tenor. In this way, like a singing parrot, I built up a chunk of Torah which would take about twenty minutes to get through, unaccompanied except for the droning of the elder members of the congregation who droned along with everything. Perhaps they would drown me out? I would sing in Hebrew, of course, with no idea of what I was singing. I also learned to 'lay' *teffilin*, a complicated winding of leather straps around wrists and forehead, which Orthodox Jews perform each dawn. I had never seen my father do it and knew that I would never do it. The rabbi was obliged to show me that and many other things, which perhaps he knew I would forget the moment I had been barmitzvah-ed. I kept to myself the guilty secret that after my day in the synagogue, I would never set foot in the place again. This was the light at the end of my tunnel, my liberation from the Jewish religion, or any religion. So much for the most important event in a Jewish boy's life.

*

As I prepared for my barmitzvah, I was also undergoing a course of electric shock treatment for flat feet at a hospital in Haverstock Hill. Both feet were placed in a pan of water with electric coils, which had currents passed through them, causing the feet to scrunch and unscrunch. I would watch this involuntary twitch, worried that the current might affect my brain.

On the way home from the hospital one afternoon, I was staring out of the top of the bus as it crawled up the

Edgware Road when I recognised Grandma advancing up the street. It was the first time I had seen her walking in the street like everybody else and it came as a shock. She had pulled a black satin cloche down almost over her eyes and had to hold her head high to see from beneath it. Her rolling gait defiantly used the very centre of the pavement; her belief in her own dignity and importance somehow affected the people around her and they unconsciously moved out of her way. I was afraid that people might laugh at her as each gust of wind allowed her white bloomers to peek from beneath her skirt.

Watching her, squirming with a mixture of pride and shame at her not knowing I was spying on her, I wondered whether I was proud of my family or ashamed of them. Did I think I was somehow better? Before I could feel any guiltier, I jumped off the bus and ran towards Grandma. Her face lit up when she recognised me.

''Allo, darlin',' she cried, dropping her shopping to give me the usual forceful hug. She kissed her special suction kisses all over my face, her eyes bright. 'Were you comin' to see *me*? I'm shoppin'.'

'No, I'm just on my way home from the hospital, Grandma.'

Her eyes popped. 'Oooh, my *God*! What's *wrong* with you?'

'Nothing. Just flat feet.'

We had a little chat and I kissed her goodbye, deciding to take the Underground home. I had to cross the road and I saw a look of panic crossing Grandma's face. A young grandson crossing a main road could only mean instant death by lorry or bus.

'Be careful! Be careful!' she began to chant, her face twisted in worry. 'Be *care*ful, darlin'.' She looked each way at the traffic, eyes widening, presenting an agonised expression to me.

I saw a gap in the traffic and leapt into the road, calling back over my shoulder, 'Don't worry, Grandma, I'll be careful.'

'Oooh, my *God*! Be *care*ful – look the other way – *wait*!

Oooh!' Her voice rose in volume and treble and she clutched at her throat as if she were strangling.

I had reached the centre of the road and began to look for a gap in the traffic coming the other way. People were staring at Grandma, frowning at her cries.

'Ooh, my *God*, be *care*ful, darlin'!'

I groaned. How had I trapped myself into this? Everyone turned to stare, wondering why this bulky woman in a 1920s cloche was screaming at the boy in the road.

'My *God*, watch where you're going!'

I eventually made it to the other side and looked back to see Grandma waving, clutching at her heart, fanning herself in relief and reassuring passers-by that her grandson, the one on the other side of the street who was so handsome and who played the piano like Liberace or better, was safe. There was a lull in the traffic's noise and Grandma took a deep breath.

''Oward?' she screamed. ''*Oward*?'

I looked across. 'What?'

It seemed to me that everyone on the street had turned to her, waiting to hear what she had to say. 'Don't forget to keep yer *bowels* open!' she cried. I scurried into the Underground, my cheeks burning.

4

The *Simcha*

The barmitzvah took over our lives. The guest-list was constantly being added to and eventually reached close to five hundred. I suppose I should have realised that my father didn't have five hundred friends and that this barmitzvah was not a celebration of my manhood but a public relations exercise for the handbag factory. Dad was inviting the great names of British handbag retailing – head buyers for Harrods, Marshall and Snelgrove, Dickens and Jones, people he barely knew. Instead of dining these potential clients at good restaurants, he felt it would flatter them to be included in a family affair. Orders would be bound to follow. We stopped eating in the dining room, since the table was piled with boxes of invitations, cream envelopes, RSVP cards and sheets of pristine postage-stamps. No general pored over plans more carefully than my parents with their table plan, my grandparents checking and approving any changes.

I accompanied my mother to some of her fittings for a spectacular purple silk ball gown, the bodice of which was being embroidered by hand. Some thirty young people would be invited after dinner, for the dance.

It had always been Dad's ambition to supply Marks and Spencer with handbags. When he heard that the brother-in-law of a cousin worked in their accounts department, he used this rather tenuous connection to invite him. The poor man would be placed at one of the top tables. The nearer the top table, the more flattered these business connections would be, the more likely to place an order. At least, that was the theory.

Everyone had their own personal ambition for this barmitzvah: my father hoping to win new clients, my sister hoping to meet a boyfriend, my mother hoping to wear the most beautiful dress, my brother hoping to smoke his first cigar and get drunk for the first time. I just prayed to get through it.

*

The barmitzvah's two days of events were recorded on colour film and projected on the sitting-room wall so many times that they are engraved, like steel etched with acid, on my memory. That plump, shiny-cheeked little boy in miniature dinner-jacket and bow-tie was like a prototype for a human being that never came about, for I grew up very differently to the man my parents had envisaged.

Every Jewish function has its mishaps – a fat little girl in thick-lensed spectacles throwing up over the dance floor, a senile aunt locking herself in the lavatory – but mine had just one small scandal, barely noticed at the time, like an atom bomb tested underground in a desert. Muffled, but with terrible reverberations later. You could say it destroyed my family.

*

After dinner, toasts to the Queen and the State of Israel were proposed and drunk to. I made a speech in a high, nervous voice, which was recorded for posterity on a twelve-inch record. The band began to retune, sounding tired from the mixture of Israeli folkloric tunes and New Orleans jazz they had been playing. The doors were opened and the young people invited for the dance were ushered into the rooms, shyly taking gulps of the cigar- and perfume-laden air. They were mostly friends of my sister or Uncle Jack. My mother fanned Grandma with a souvenir menu on which my smiling portrait appeared. Grandma sat ramrod-straight with a fixed smile on her face, now and then giving a small wave to the tables facing her. She wore emerald satin draped around her stout body, topped by a brown mink stole. Amongst the new entrants was a pretty blonde girl who began to dance with Uncle Jack. It had been his brave intention to introduce his new girlfriend to the family, but he had baulked at the last moment and not introduced her to anyone. To cover his confusion, he stayed close to her all evening.

'Lovely girl,' I heard one of Grandma's cronies mutter to another as they peered at Jack's date.

'Doesn't look Jewish, though,' said another, peering closer.

'She's a *shiksa*,' the whisper went through the room.

I had other things on my mind. I could see from my father's face that the Marks and Spencer connection hadn't paid off. Possibly he had grabbed the guest the moment he had arrived, instead of waiting for him to have a few drinks.

Throughout the evening, the great names of handbag retailing had approached me, winking as they slipped envelopes containing cheques into my pocket. It remained only for my mother and me to open the dance with the stiff waltz we had been practising for weeks. The home movie shows a sweaty little boy clutching his mother's waist as she smiles fixedly over his head, a cruel parody of the Oedipus complex, I thought later, watching the film. My father led my blushing sister onto the floor and we suddenly changed partners, my parents waltzing off as I clumsily led Rachel. 'And now, *everybody* dance!' urged the toastmaster, and the band's volume rose to a crescendo as couples milled over the floor. A fat Californian cousin elbowed my sister out of the way and grabbed me. Grandma leaned forward from the top table, trying to focus on the girl her son was dancing with. She seemed disturbed. The Californian cousin whirled me in the other direction and I lost sight of Grandma.

*

A week after the event, our house reeked of decaying centre-pieces. They were dead but my mother couldn't quite bring herself to throw them away. It would mean admitting that the long-awaited event was truly over. I had written three hundred thank-you notes. By snooping amongst the receipts, I learned that the barmitzvah had cost close to a thousand pounds. The total of my gifts, mostly cheques, came to around the same sum. I found nothing ominous in this, but years later when I tried to claim my money, I learned that my father had used it to pay for the party.

I sensed my mother's tremendous let-down. She had been planning the event for so long she now felt she had nothing to look forward to.

'In three years' time, you'll have Lawrence's barmitzvah.' I tried to cheer her up.

'I don't want to spend my life planning functions, darling.' She smiled sadly, stubbing out a cigarette. 'I want to work.'

'Work?' I was amazed. 'What kind of work?'

She looked at me helplessly. 'That's just it, darling. I don't know. Not with your father and not in the factory, that's for sure.'

To cheer herself up, she planned a series of evenings at home to screen the ninety-minute film of the barmitzvah so that guests could see what they had looked like. Each guest could relive the entire evening, and tea and cakes would be served. It meant that we had to sit through the film six times.

*

Since I was now officially a man, I reasoned I could visit Grandma on my own. Finding myself in her neighbourhood one afternoon later that month, I rang her bell. Mary, her Irish maid, answered.

'Oh, thank goodness 'tis you, Mr Howard,' she began in her breathless brogue, 'I thought it might be Mr G home early and here Mrs G's taking a funny turn.'

She led the way down the corridor and I followed apprehensively. A 'funny turn' in our family could mean anything from a mild headache to death. The family had always been squeamish about illness, not treating it or even acknowledging it. People passed kidney-stones lying in agony on a couch. My family paid doctors *not* to treat them.

'Drinking all afternoon,' Mary muttered, as we entered the kitchen. 'Your grandson!' she announced loudly. 'Come all this way to see you.'

I wondered why she was shouting. Grandma was sitting at the kitchen table, slumped over a teacup, which smelled of whisky. She wore a crumpled white nightgown.

'Been sitting there like that all day,' Mary marvelled, shaking her head.

'Hello Grandma.'

As I leaned to kiss her unpowdered cheek, there was a distinct smell of sweat. Not dirty sweat, this was aggravation sweat. Without powder, her complexion was sallow. Her red-rimmed eyes hardly took me in, her creased gown fell in dramatic folds making a monumental statue out of her, a symbolic figure portraying 'Misery' perhaps, or 'Despair'.

'Are you all right?' I said.

She looked a hundred years old. Although the kitchen chandelier was switched on, the room seemed dim, as if she had the power to drain the light from it.

'What's the matter?' I asked her. She remained staring into her teacup. 'Grandma?' I tried again. 'What's the matter?'

'What's the mattah? What's the mattah?' she mocked my careful tone, sitting straight up and glaring at me. 'My son's going with a *shiksa*, that's what's the mattah!'

I flinched at the word, embarrassed that she would say it in front of Mary. '*Shiksa*' only meant 'non-Jewish girl', but it had negative overtones. In Grandma's mind, Mary had become more Jewish than any Jew. Like the Gentile servants hired by Orthodox Jews to switch on electric lights on the sabbath, she understood all the rites and taboos. Even extending to marrying out of one's faith, which she knew for Grandma was the worst imaginable tragedy.

'Surely if they love each other –' I began.

'*Love*? Do me a favour!' Grandma cut me off, fixing me with glittering eyes. 'Love soon goes out the window.' She fumbled for her handkerchief and gave a noisy, defeated blow into it. 'Love!' she said again, with the utmost contempt. Then she shot me a begging look, almost as if she expected me to reassure her.

This was beyond my capabilities. I didn't see what she was making such a fuss about. We had never been that religious – for all I knew, I would marry a non-Jewish girl myself. Grandma dabbed her eyes and when she stared at me, her irises seemed to have shattered into grey and green shards.

'My Jack was fourteen years old before 'e knew what night was,' she said suddenly. She blew her nose. ''E used to ask: "Mum? What *is* night?" 'Is curtains was drawn by four in the afternoon in the winter. I wouldn't let 'im see it was dark outside.'

I nodded, trying to follow her train of thought. This maternal protection from the dark sounded insane to me. It was just one of the many crazy tenets Grandma tried to force people to agree with, in this case that day was good and night somehow bad.

'And for *what*?' she demanded. 'The minute they grow up, they turn around and do something like *this*!'

'Young people fall in love without thinking,' Mary said.

'Don't you want him to be happy?' I asked.

Grandma laughed. ''Ow could 'e be 'appy with little *yocks* for children?' she asked, holding out her empty teacup to Mary as if she were in a speakeasy. Mary shook her head and splashed a little Scotch into the cup, tut-tutting and rolling her eyes.

'But … *you* only go to synagogue once a year,' I said. 'You don't keep a kosher kitchen. You aren't even that religious.' Grandma stared at me pityingly.

'Don't they teach you anything in those Hebrew classes?' she asked. 'The religion comes through the mother. If the mother's a *shiksa*, the children are *goy*.'

Mary confirmed this with an authoritative nod. 'Why

don't you have a little lie-down, Mrs G?' she suggested. 'Your grandson will help you to bed –'

Grandma jerked around to look at her. 'What time is it?' she asked.

'Nearly six o'clock and Mr G expected home at any moment now,' Mary said quickly.

'And since when did I go to bed at six o'clock?' Grandma asked. 'No one is 'elpin' me to bed. It's not bedtime yet.' She held out her teacup again but this time Mary did not pour.

'You know what it does to you on an empty stomach, Mrs G,' she warned. 'You'll have heartburn for days. It would be better for all of youse if you just slept it off, now. What'll Mr G think?'

'What do *I* care what 'e thinks,' Grandma jeered. 'It's *'is* son too, isn't it? They'll be *'is yock* grandchildren too, won't they?'

'Why don't you meet this girl, get to know her?' I said, sitting in the chair beside her. 'She seemed very nice.'

'Beautiful girl, sure,' Mary gasped. 'Tall, slim, friendly.'

'If they're really in love –' I began again.

Grandma cut me off with a groan. 'Do me a favour … *love*!' she said. 'You think *I* was in love when *I* got married?'

'Yes,' I answered confidently. 'And I think you and Grandpa still love each other very much.'

Grandma stared at me for a moment, then turned to Mary. ''E thinks I was in love with Mr G, Mary,' she gasped. ''Ere.' She thrust her teacup at Mary. 'Pour yourself one, too.'

This was to make sure that Mary continued to agree with her. For my sake, Mary glanced doubtfully at the bottle before pouring a generous shot and swallowing it as professionally as Grandma had done. These two must have drunk away many an afternoon together.

''E thinks I was in love, Mary.' Grandma shook her head, grabbing the bottle and pouring herself another half a cup.

Mary's eyes darted this way and that and she began to

mutter to herself at an incredibly fast rate. Although she was Grandma's confidante, she had the sense that she could not say anything against my grandfather in front of me, so she said hesitantly, 'He's a very kind man, Mr G.'

'Very kind man, do me a favour,' Grandma gurgled. 'You think I was in love?' She faced me, staring directly into my eyes, drunk and frank. 'You want to know why I married your grandfather?' she asked.

I didn't really want to know. I wanted the family secrets to remain secret for a little while longer.

Grandpa's key turning in the front door ended my dilemma. We all waited silently, listening to his footsteps down the long corridor towards the kitchen. At the doorway, Grandpa stopped, blinking in the light.

'You here?' he asked, coming in and kissing me. He gazed at Grandma. 'What sort of state are you in?' He checked his watch. 'It's not even six.'

There was an expectant pause. It lasted a long time. Finally, unable to contain herself, Mary burst out in a torrent of words: 'Oh, she's been drinking all afternoon, Mr G. She's that upset about Mr Jack and all. Here I've been tellin' her it's bad for her stomach what with her not having had a bite to eat all day, and she not listening, no, not listening at all.'

She stopped suddenly, staring eagerly at Grandpa. He unfolded his *Evening News* and glanced at the front page.

'I've 'ad a few drinks, Max,' Grandma announced. Grandpa sat down heavily.

Mary snorted. 'A *few*?' she cried. 'Oh, Mr G, I shouldn't be surprised if she's not drunk her way through the best part of a bottle. An entire bottle of whisky in an afternoon, sure.'

We all watched Grandpa. Even Grandma appeared vaguely interested in how he was going to react. If he were my father, I thought, there would be a short countdown to an explosion. But Grandpa was Grandpa. He turned a page of his newspaper.

'So what's for dinner?' he asked. Grandma glanced over at Mary.

'We could warm up those chicken legs, Mrs G,' Mary suggested brightly. 'Would you fancy chicken legs, Mr G?' she asked Grandpa. 'With a few potatoes?'

Grandpa grunted his acceptance of this. Then he got up with a sigh and left the kitchen. We heard him bustling around the bedroom, changing into his slippers, entering the bathroom to wash. The two women exchanged a quick glance and Mary began burrowing in the fridge to find the chicken legs.

'You'd better go now, darlin',' Grandma muttered wearily. 'Before there's murders. Mary will see you out. Your grandfather doesn't like me drinking so early in the day. Go on now.'

'Okay.' I leaned to kiss her. 'Goodbye, Grandma.'

'Oh, she's a terror when she gets started on the whisky, Mr Howard,' Mary babbled all the way down the dark corridor. 'Been on and on about Mr Jack and his girlfriend and what might happen if they might choose to marry, and a lovely girl she is too, slim, pretty, blonde and all. I knew Mr G wouldn't like it when he come home and found her like that. Wait until Mr Jack gets home, later! She'll be crying and screaming … what an evening we're in for.'

She unlocked the front door, her hand resting on it. 'My nerves can't stand this, Mr Howard,' she told me, 'you can't know what it's like working for her. If it wasn't for my poor son I'd leave, I really would.' She had an adult son who was slightly retarded and she paid for him to attend a specialist school.

'I'm sorry, Mary.' I touched her arm awkwardly, and she stood aside. 'I'll come by in a few days when things have quietened down.'

'Oh, they must!' said Mary. 'I can't go on like this. My nerves just won't take it.'

On the bus home, I felt very adult, having seen my grandmother drunk and dishevelled, not even trying to pretend, for my sake, that everything was all right. Everyone in the family had always obeyed her wishes, I thought. She had a force that made them obey. She would withhold her love if they didn't: emotional blackmail.

Without her approval, they seemed unable to function. Until now. It was surprising that someone as young and meek as Uncle Jack could defy her. Would Freud perhaps say Jack had deliberately chosen to fall in love with a girl his mother could not possibly approve of? As a way of escaping her?

5

Getting the *Shiksa* out of his System

After all the screenings of the barmitzvah movie, it was a relief to have the spotlight off my shiny face and onto the gloomy but determined face of Uncle Jack. Now that he was involved in a forbidden love affair, we looked upon him in awe, as if he had contracted some rare disease. Grandma and Grandpa concentrated on the best way of 'getting the *shiksa* out of his system' as if Uncle Jack was passing a kidney-stone or suffering severe constipation, both frequent and painful occurrences in our family. Jack's affliction was never given her real name of Christine. It struck me that my family was somewhat callous.

For this crisis only, Grandma allowed some cronies to proffer advice, not that she had any intention of following it. She had supervised every aspect of Jack's life, arranging blind dates with Jewish girls and introductions to Jewish youth clubs, forbidding him to frequent dance halls, pubs or any place where the clientele was not Jewish. Although her friends shared this experience of steering their sons through the land-mines of non-Jewish girls, Grandma refused to compare these boys to Jack; they were not nearly so handsome nor as good a catch. She did not realise that she had given Jack such an impossibly high opinion of his own 'film-star' looks that he felt that he deserved a beautiful blonde *shiksa*, one as like Marilyn Monroe as possible.

Finally, Grandma settled for the 'getting her out of his system' theory. Instead of forbidding all contact with said *shiksa*, you let your son see as much of her as he wanted. Just as a person addicted to chocolate might gorge until they never wanted to set eyes on chocolate again, Grandma had high hopes that Jack would go off Christine if she were no longer forbidden fruit. She added one rule: he must sleep in his own bed at night. Somehow, that made the affair seem a little less sinful. But a beautiful young girl cannot be compared to a bar of chocolate, and Uncle Jack became more besotted than ever.

It was Grandpa's turn next. He suddenly gave his son a silver-grey Jaguar. It was like an exquisite piece of sculpture sitting in the road outside their flat. I used to stare at it, seeing the crouching animal in its sensuous lines. I was not quite sure what this gift was all about. A reminder that if he obeyed his parents, there was plenty more where that came from? But all that happened was that Jack drove his *shiksa* around town in his new car.

Months passed. It seemed we would never have a normal Saturday tea at Grandma's again. Nor ever hear Grandma laugh again. The problem had become too grave to discuss before us. A new solution was being secretly planned. It was drastic and expensive, but the grown-ups seemed to think it might work.

*

By spring of the following year, our Saturday teas had still not yet returned to their previous festive format. But each Saturday we all met up at five o'clock outside Grandma's flat, always hopeful that something more than tea and biscuits would be served, and that Grandma would be smiling and welcoming once again. On this particular Saturday in April, my mother had to ring the doorbell several times before the door was opened almost reluctantly by Grandpa.

'I thought I told you not to come,' he said, and I felt for the first time the shock of not being welcome in my grandparents' home.

'It'll cheer up Mum to see the children,' my mother insisted, ushering us inside.

Somehow, we knew it was not the moment to run

whooping down the corridor as we usually did. The flat was dark and silent and we stopped dead on finding the kitchen empty and unlit. Something terrible must have happened, I thought. My brother and sister ran back to the dining room, but I stared at the thin, grey light that stole in through the kitchen window, just showing that the table was bare.

'I didn't get out to the shops,' Grandpa said. 'I could make some tea.'

He switched on the chandelier. The kitchen, usually so hot from steaming kettle or simmering soup, was cold. We huddled together, not sitting down.

'Why did you come?' he asked again.

'I thought if she saw the children it would –' my mother began.

'Ha! She won't even see *me*,' Grandpa said.

'Where is Grandma?' I asked him.

Behind Grandpa's shoulder, an apparition suddenly appeared. A ghostly white figure drifted by behind him and floated down the corridor towards the bathroom.

'Grandma!' I cried. There was no reply.

I ran into the corridor just in time to catch the last of a trailing white train of nightgown disappearing around a door. I turned to Grandpa. He gave a meaningful look at my mother, shaking his head. In his white shirt, tie, buttoned waistcoat and dark trousers, he lent a touch of formality to the strange afternoon.

'But what –?' I said.

'Sshhh,' my father hushed me.

We all moved into the corridor. It was a long wait during which no one spoke. The lavatory flushed noisily, then we waited several long moments before the doorknob began to turn. Whether she knew it or not, Grandma was a master of timing. The bathroom door finally opened and in place of the extrovert, excitable woman with orange hair, red nails and scarlet mouth, there appeared a heavy, grey personage whose face was colourless, whose eyes were sunk in dark caverns and whose cheeks were wet with tears. She trudged past us without acknowledging our presence and disappeared into her bedroom, shutting the door behind her.

'Has Uncle Jack died?' my brother blurted out.

'Shut up!' my father yelled, slapping his head.

'Shut your mouth,' Grandpa said, pretending to spit. This spitting was a Jewish custom to ensure that what was said would not happen. Lawrence rubbed his head, too surprised to cry. Grandpa stared gravely at us. He cleared his throat.

'Uncle Jack has gone to America,' he finally announced. 'He's going to join his brother. He'll ... get to know another country for a year. He'll ... be with his brother, get some experience, and ...' he gave a little nod, half to himself, '... he'll get the *shiksa* out of his system.'

The full import of the news slowly sank in as we watched Grandpa struggle with cups, kettle and tea-strainer, rebuffing my mother's attempts to help. We got the full story as he prepared our scanty meal. Jack was – at that very moment – in mid-air, over the Atlantic. If Grandma was worried about me crossing Edgware Road under her watchful eye, it could scarcely be imagined how she felt about her favourite son flying. She wasn't simply worried – any mother could be worried – she was actually grieving for what she saw as the inevitable accident, for how could such a heavy machine remain aloft for so many hours? She could see the bold headlines, the list of dead, the return of a signet ring or wristwatch dredged from the ocean bed or found in the mangled wreckage. And although our first impulse was to laugh, her grief was so real that we soon assumed the funereal air that filled the flat. She was only doing what I had done when I had lain awake at night picturing my mother's death. Perhaps she felt that this premature grief was a kind of insurance against an accident, like carrying an umbrella to make sure it didn't rain.

They had decided that if Grandma were going to grieve throughout her son's journey, it would be better if she grieved for the fifteen hours of a flight rather than the six days of an ocean crossing. What Grandpa hadn't bargained for was the grief starting from the moment he bought Jack's ticket. For the past ten days, Grandma had stopped sleeping, eating, talking or dressing. Meanwhile, Jack had packed his suitcase, visited aunts to say goodbye, spent hours with Christine and watched his inconsolable mother's tears. It must have been strange for him, living with someone who acted as if he had died several days ago.

It was understood that Grandma would emerge from this mourning only on receiving the phone call from New York announcing Jack's safe arrival. Various guesses were made as to when this would be.

'It'll take a while before he gets to a phone,' Grandpa pointed out, waiting for the kettle to boil. 'You pass through Immigration. Then Customs. They do you a whole favour to let you into that goddamned country,' he chuckled. 'Then they must get the car, *schlepp* the luggage into it, drive home, find a parking space …' He seemed to be trying to convince himself that we were in for a long wait. Looking up at me, he said, 'Maybe Howard wouldn't mind buying us some bread?' I agreed and he led me to the front door, handing me a pound note.

'You remember Aunt Hilda, don't you?' he whispered. I nodded. 'Be a good boy and ring her bell. Tell her Jack's gone to New York. That's why she hasn't heard from me. Tell her I'll try to pop in tomorrow. Keep it between us, okay?'

'Okay!'

Feeling rather important, I ran downstairs and bought a loaf of bread from the nearest grocery shop. Then I found Hilda's front door and rang her bell. There was a wait as she came down the steep flight of stairs to open the door. Her pencilled eyebrows shot up when she saw me and she broke into a smile.

'Howard!' she cried. 'What a lovely surprise.'

She pulled me to her and I kissed her cheek, which smelled of face powder. Her hair was tightly pinned back into a bun with a fine net over it. Her eyes searched mine from behind her narrow spectacles, widening slightly.

'Nothing wrong, is there, dear?' she asked.

'Oh no,' I assured her. 'It's just that Uncle Jack's gone to America for a year to be with Uncle Frankie. They're waiting for a phone call from New York to hear that he's arrived safely.'

'Oh!' She was surprised but quickly controlled her expression. 'Oh, he's gone to New York, has he?' Her voice suddenly sounded falsely cheerful. 'They'll miss him, won't they?' Her eyes searched mine as though I knew more than I was saying. 'Is she in a bit of a state, then, Mrs G?'

I nodded. 'She's taken to her bed.'

'Y-e-s-s …' she said, half to herself, '… she would, wouldn't she?' She gave a long sigh, shaking her head. 'But … a year! What on earth will he do there for a year?'

She stared at me with such an expectant expression that I found myself blurting out: 'He's gone to get the *shiksa* out of his system.' Even before her face darkened and I got the dirtiest look I'd ever received from a grown-up, I knew I had said the wrong thing.

'That "*shiksa*",' she finally said, handling the word as if it dangled from tongs, 'happens to be in my flat right now, crying her eyes out.'

Grabbing my arm in a firm grip, she hustled me up the staircase to her flat. Once inside, she walked me down a corridor to a room at the end. She knocked gently on the door.

'Christine?' she called. 'We've got a visitor.' Turning to me, she said, 'I think you ought to meet the *shiksa* they've sent your uncle away to forget.'

The door was opened by a pale, pretty blonde girl. I recognised her as Jack's companion from my barmitzvah dance. She was quite tall, with a small, upturned nose and eyes so blue they were almost turquoise. Their red rims and bloodshot whites made them even more intense.

'This is Howard, Christine,' Hilda introduced us. 'Mr G's grandson. He's just told me about Jack. Now I understand why you've been so miserable this last week.'

'How do you do, Howard.' Christine held out her hand and we shook gravely. She looked at Hilda regretfully. 'I didn't want to upset you, darling. I knew you'd hear about it soon enough. Has he reached New York yet?' she asked me.

'Not yet. We're waiting at Grandma's until she gets his phone call,' I told her. I was puzzled, trying to put all the pieces together. Why was this girl living with Aunt Hilda?

Christine made herself smile. 'It was so nice of you to come, Howard. Are you going to give him some tea, Hilda?' She dabbed her eyes and looked as if she were about to cry again. 'Will you excuse me?' she asked. 'I don't want to seem rude, but I really need to be alone.'

'Of course. I'll bring you some tea later,' Hilda said.

'Goodbye, Howard. Nice to meet you,' Christine said to me, then, breaking into sobs, she quickly closed the door. We walked back to the sitting room.

'I'm terribly sorry,' I said. 'Calling her a *shiksa*. I didn't mean it to be rude.'

Hilda touched my arm. 'We can't all be Jewish, can we, dear? *Shiksa* only means a non-Jewish girl, doesn't it? I'm one, too, except I'm no longer a girl.' She gave a little giggle.

'So you're not my aunt?' I asked.

'No dear. But I don't mind you calling me Auntie.'

'Is Christine … a relation?' I asked.

Hilda's eyes stared unseeingly over my shoulder towards Christine's room. 'Ever since her dear mother died – she was my best friend – I've felt like a mother to her. Didn't have any children of my own, y'see. She's such a lovely girl. Wouldn't harm a soul. Her misfortune was to fall in love with your uncle.'

I nodded gravely. 'So it's like Romeo and Juliet?' I asked.

Hilda laughed. 'Oh, I wouldn't know about that. I'm not an intellectual. Christine's educated. She's read ever so many books. Got all her GCEs, too.'

'Why does she live here?' I asked.

'Well, she had to work in London, didn't she?' Hilda said. 'Wanted all the bright lights. She's ambitious. Comes from a little town up North – you'd never know from her accent, would you? Not like me. Everything was going so

well for her. Her father was so pleased I could give her a
room and I truly do love her as if she's my own daughter.'
She broke off, her eyes filling with tears.

'Grandpa says he'll come by tomorrow,' I said quickly.

'That's right,' Hilda said briskly. 'Tell him not to worry.
Will you have some tea? I could do with a cup.'

'No, thank you, I'd better be getting back. They've got
no bread.' I showed her the bag with the loaf in it.

'No *bread*?' Hilda repeated, shocked. 'They *must* be in a
state. Well, things will calm down when he calls, won't
they?'

'I suppose so,' I agreed.

Hilda leaned to kiss my cheek. 'I'm sorry I dragged you
upstairs like that,' she apologised. 'It just took me by
surprise. You see what kind of girl Christine is. She hadn't
told me. I wondered why she was moping in her room. It's
not like her. Then you arrive and tell me that.' She shook
her head. 'Oh, it's a terrible thing to do to two lovely young
people who love each other, I don't care what their religion is.'

'I agree,' I said.

She smiled and waved me off. I hurried back to
Grandma's flat. I was a little angry with Grandpa for
letting me in for all that, but I also felt firmly on the side of
the beleaguered lovers. Why had Grandpa told me that
Hilda was my aunt? I reminded myself not always to
believe what adults told me.

'We're staying here until Uncle Jack phones,' my
mother told me, opening the front door.

'Oh … must we?' I groaned.

'Darling, we'll be keeping Grandpa company,' my
mother explained. 'Grandma will drive him crazy if the
plane's delayed or anything.'

In the kitchen, she unwrapped the bread and began to
make cheese and tomato sandwiches, cutting off the crusts.
Crusts were only removed on serious occasions. Grandpa
took a cup of tea to the door of the bedroom and knocked
on it.

'I don't want nothin',' we heard Grandma croak

through it. No tea, no comfort, nothing would be allowed to distract her from these last excruciating hours of suffering.

The time dragged. After the sandwiches and tea and an hour of waiting, we were allowed to open one of the boxes of liqueur chocolates, which Grandma saved in a tower of twenty atop a nest of tables in the smaller sittingroom. These tributes from friends had always been considered too good to open, and were years old. My mother tore the cellophane from the lowest box and we attacked the dusty contents only to find the chocolates had all dried out. We sucked the sugary shells and tried to guess which liqueur they had once contained. Soon, we began to feel slightly sick. Rachel pretended to fall asleep on the red brocade dining-room couch. She believed it was terribly grown-up to be able to drop off to sleep at any time, but we knew she was only pretending. Now and then the doorbell sounded. Friends who, despite strict instructions to stay away, were 'too concerned' to obey. Grandma had various cronies that I thought of as the Brass Ladies, since their permed hair and jewellery was bright yellow-gold.

'Heard anything yet?' they whispered hopefully, beating a hasty retreat when Grandpa shook his head, casting curious glances at Grandma's closed bedroom door as if they would catch a glimpse of a woman who loved her son so much she had taken to her bed until she heard he was safe.

I stole into Uncle Jack's room to seek something to read. There was a copy of *Esquire* which I grabbed. The neatly-made bed and empty clothes-stand had already taken on the aspect of a shrine. Would the year's absence really get Christine (I would never say or think '*shiksa*' again) out of his system? Wasn't there a saying – I wished I had discussed it with Hilda – 'absence makes the heart grow fonder'? I stretched out on the small sitting-room couch, layers of thick transparent plastic and white sheeting between me and the burgundy brocade. I must have fallen asleep, for much later I remember the phone waking me. I lay there, listening to it, wondering why

Grandma hadn't picked up at the first ring. She seemed to let it ring many times, stretching out the moment of relief like a man dying of thirst in the desert might hold the brimming cup of water proffered by his rescuers for several long moments before actually sipping.

Finally: ''Allo?' I heard her croak. ''Allo?' Her mouth dry from not having had any tea, her throat aching and her voice hoarse. ''Allo?' Her voice rising after a few notes, becoming almost a scream. ''ALLO?' Now it was a scream. With each ''Allo?' I sat up a little straighter on the couch and I was sure everyone else was sitting up too, holding their breath. After all, this might be an airline official calling to inform the nearest relatives of an accident.

''Allo darlin'?'

And then her screams of joy and relief, protestations of love, cries and sobs as she conveyed to her son how much she had suffered, how she had willed the heavy aircraft to stay aloft. All this rang out over the transatlantic wire before she suddenly realised how much the call must be costing and abruptly rang off. She reinstalled herself in the kitchen at one-thirty in the morning, cutting up vegetables and pieces of meat to simmer in a huge pot. She discovered food that Grandpa hadn't seen. She was ravenously hungry and convinced that we must be too. The life flowed back into her face and limbs as she sipped tea, laughed, wept or reached out to hug one of us. She lost twenty years of age in the blink of an eye. 'The brothers are together!' she kept announcing, over and over again. The triumph on her face at once again outwitting fate!

6

Enter Two Adoring Female Eccentrics

As if they had been awaiting their cues off-stage, two more eccentric females, both offering unconditional approval, entered my life: Violet Dorothy Goodfellow, my piano teacher, and Ursula, our new Swedish *au pair*, the first adults outside my family to take me seriously.

Miss Goodfellow burst into our home in the middle of a violent thunderstorm, soaked through, and proceeded to remove scarves, shawl, cape and dress to stand steaming in a black slip before the red bars of the electric fire as I attempted to play my scales for her. It was the most exciting thing that had ever happened to me, because she acted as if I were man of the world enough not to stare. I was too nervous to play well and stumbled through the scales, one eye on her.

'Very good, dear,' she nodded, when I had finished. 'Now, play them again – a little more *carefully* this time.'

An elocution and piano teacher, Miss Goodfellow was taken on to teach us piano only, but her carefully enunciated vowels were contagious and I was soon speaking the Queen's English, as opposed to Grandma's Pearly Queen's Cockney. I must have sounded like a stuck-up little snob and it deepened the difference I felt between myself and my family.

During my second lesson, I confided to Miss Goodfellow my ambition to be an artist. She nodded, as if it were perfectly normal.

'Howard,' she announced grandly, 'from the moment I met you, I could see you had the Artistic Temperament.'

'Have I?' I beamed. I felt awed, as if it might prove something to live up to.

Neither Lawrence nor Rachel had the Artistic Temperament and soon gave up their lessons. Since Miss Goodfellow assured my mother that I showed exceptional talent (one of the easiest things in the world of which to convince her), I took over their lessons. I was to have three per week and learn a wide selection of pieces, from Brahms to Winifred Atwell, Miss Goodfellow deeming that 'boogie-woogie' strengthened the left hand.

I fell a little in love with Miss Goodfellow. A dowdier, bulkier version of Greta Garbo, she dressed in the style in which Willesden residents expected piano teachers to dress, trailing long, floating scarves, throwing a dramatic cloak over one shoulder. She favoured tiny black shoes that resembled Victorian skating-boots and her strong scent was of violets. I loved her long, red-lacquered nails clicking over the keys as she wandered off into a bit of Gershwin or Cole Porter. She could easily have earned her living as a cocktail pianist in some dimly-lit hotel bar. To me, she was the essence of sophistication, a doorway into the adult world. No one apart from my mother listened to what I said with such intense interest. Lighting a cigarette, she would inhale, narrow her eyes, and concentrate on me as she slowly exhaled the blue haze.

I poured my heart out during our five-minute breaks, which soon took on all the confessional aspects of analysis. And, just like an analyst, Miss Goodfellow kept a beady eye on her tiny jewelled watch, steering me back to the keyboard when our time was up. To all my whines about the lack of understanding from my family, she would screw up her eyes behind her narrow spectacles and command:

'Persevere!' Then, after a short pause, 'Brahms.'

I pestered my mother for details of her private life. Her age? 'Around fifty?' my mother guessed. Her marital status? 'She's a spinster,' my mother confirmed. I nodded sadly.

How strange that such a fascinating woman should have been left on the shelf. Her fuchsia lipstick, violet scents, trailing scarves and black-stockinged legs surely made her an object of desire? 'She's had her chances,' Mum said. 'She once told me she was crossed in love.' I was too proud to ask what 'crossed in love' meant and it added even more mystery to my teacher.

Ursula, the latest in a long line of domestic helps, was the second approving female. Irish girls had given way to more democratic *au pairs* who refused heavy housework. My mother now did it, throwing herself into it with relish and energy. When we were on holiday she even scrubbed hotel baths with Vim before allowing us to bathe. Ursula – a Swedish Flower Child a whole decade before the term was invented – braided her thick blonde hair and danced barefoot on our lawn. We spied on her through the white net curtains. 'It is very good for the feet,' she told my mother, who sniffed doubtfully and said, 'Yes, but is it good for the *grass*?'

I liked Ursula because she was gentle and often picked up my sketchbook to leaf carefully through, peering at my daubs with great seriousness. An art critic who did not know the meaning of the verb 'to criticise', she believed any artistic expression was good. I thought my sketches were being discovered by someone who knew real talent when she saw it. It felt wonderful after the sarcastic remarks my art teacher at school, Mr Gough, usually made. My last composition had been the angels ascending and descending Jacob's ladder in his dream from the Bible. Mr Gough had held it up and sneered: 'I think Conway intended this for *Vogue* magazine, or perhaps Hollywood.' It did look like a still from a Cecil B. De Mille movie, but when I reported the comments back to my mother, she quickly put them down to jealousy.

'He wishes he could get *his* work into a glossy magazine,' she assured me.

Now she had Ursula to agree with on my talent. 'Better than Dali,' Ursula pronounced finally. She added 'Ya!' and closed the sketchbook.

'Not better,' I protested.

'Better, ya,' she nodded. 'Mrs Conway, this boy should be at art school.'

My mother gave the sketchbook a more intent look, wagging her head as if to say, 'Hmmm, maybe he does have something …'

'Mum, I want to be an artist,' I told her, watching her frying some onions one evening.

'Shhhh,' she hushed me, eyes darting around to make sure no one had overheard. 'Wouldn't you rather be a concert pianist, darling? I can just picture you walking out onto a concert platform in white tie and tails.'

'No!' I shook my head vigorously. 'An artist.'

'Well, whatever you do, never mention this to Daddy. He won't like it at all. Try to do well at school. Maybe one day,' she squinted her eyes as if trying to picture something, 'if he's in a good mood …' She trailed off.

I didn't like this. I smarted at needing my father's permission to do what I was born to do. Had Van Gogh needed his father to be in a good mood to 'allow' him to become an artist?

*

I bumped into Hilda on the Edgware Road one evening, after visiting Grandma. She had the bright air of a blackbird, her hair glossy and dark, make-up fresh and perfect.

'Howard.' She smiled as I kissed her. 'My, you're growing tall. How are you?'

'Fine. How's Christine?' I asked.

She glanced both ways as if we might be overheard. 'A bit low,' she confided quietly. She bit her lip. 'You won't repeat anything I say? Not even to Mr G?'

'This is between you and me, Aunt Hilda,' I promised.

Her face relaxed. 'Just Hilda will do, dear.' She hustled us into the nearest café, where just a few ladies sat, sipping tea.

'I can't drink the tea at work,' Hilda sighed as she sat down. 'You know what it's like when you see it all day.' She ordered two teas from a listless waitress, then turned her bright eyes on me. 'The staff drive me mad, Howard,' she said. 'There's a feeling in this country that catering isn't quite good enough. Girls only want to be waitresses if they have no other choice. On the continent it's a respected profession.'

As if to prove the point, the waitress returned with two teas sloshing into their saucers. Hilda looked up at her, smiling sweetly. 'Would you mind bringing two *dry* saucers, dear?' She pulled her chair closer to me and breathlessly began. 'Jack writes every week.' She raised her pencilled eyebrows. 'I don't know if it's good or bad. Christine loves getting his letters, but afterwards she's ever so sad.'

Two fresh saucers arrived and were replaced under Hilda's pursed mouth. 'Try a Kunzle cake, Howard.' She indicated the selection on the table. I chose a canary-yellow one, unwrapped it and bit into its artificial sweetness. 'Do you know about first love, Howard?' she asked me. 'It can be so strong.' She leaned back, closing her eyes for a moment. 'She won't even look at anyone else – and she gets plenty of offers, believe me.' She chose a pink Kunzle cake, unwrapped it and fastidiously prised off the matching glacé cherry. 'What if Jack meets some other girl over there? Don't tell me he isn't having the time of his life in New York?' She bit into her cake. 'Any man could count himself lucky to get Christine,' she went on. 'She's got a good job and they're giving her a raise this month. Your uncle's a nice boy, but what makes your Grandma think he's God's gift?'

This was something I had sometimes wondered. We sipped our tea. 'Why does your grandmother want to ruin so many lives?' Hilda asked me.

'She thinks she's protecting lives,' I explained.

Hilda sniffed, dabbing her lips with a serviette. There was a perfect red imprint of her mouth.

'They will marry,' she said. 'I feel it in my bones. But what she has to go through first. A whole wasted year. Her poor father. He's such a nice man and so lonely now that Christine's mother's gone. He's living alone in Brighton and he can't understand what's going on up here. I've tried to explain Mrs G to him, but she's hard to explain to someone like him: he's just never met or heard of anyone quite like her.'

I touched her hand. 'Grandma will realise how much they love each other,' I promised. 'And she'll give in.'

Hilda's head jerked up, her tear-filled eyes sparkling. 'But I don't *want* her giving in,' she cried. 'Christine should be *welcomed* into your family.'

Once again I had said the wrong thing. I squirmed in my seat as Hilda blew her nose and repaired her make-up. In an attempt to change the subject, she asked about my piano lessons and my ambition to become an artist. I brought out my sketchbook and began her portrait. 'Woman eating Kunzle Cake' caught the essence of Hilda, I felt, an anxious decent woman trying to stay cheerful. But how were spectacle lenses drawn? Could a few pencil-strokes indicate reflected light? Could I capture those sharp yet kindly eyes? She stopped me when I attempted to rip out the page to give her the drawing.

'No, don't spoil your sketchbook,' she said. 'I'll be flattered to think I'm in it, Howard. I can say I knew you when.'

*

We received so much encouragement and praise from my mother that we were resigned to getting none from Dad. We came not to expect it. Rachel had decided that she wanted to become an air-hostess. It was the glamour job of the decade and had strict height and weight requirements. Rachel was tall enough but her weight was over the limit. After dieting for three months, she showed off her new, slimmer figure one evening.

'I've lost three-quarters of a stone,' she exulted, and we all applauded and cheered.

'Look, Joe, isn't it wonderful?' my mother asked my father.

Dad removed his head from the newspaper to study Rachel. 'She needs to lose another two stone,' he said dourly.

Rachel burst into tears and ran up to her room. I passed by it a few minutes later, after Mum had gone to her aid.

Rachel was face down on her bed, my mother stroking her head. 'I know how hard it is to lose weight, darling,' Mum was saying. 'Daddy does too. It's just his way of showing you –'

'Oh stop excusing him,' Rachel sniffed, sitting up red-eyed. 'He's never given me any praise, not once.'

'He doesn't want you to get a swollen head, darling,' Mum said.

'No!' Rachel blew her nose loudly. 'I don't swallow that at all.'

I crept away, thoughtfully. Dad never would be encouraging, I knew, of anything we might choose to do. Yet something in me needed to announce my intention of becoming an artist, to make it more official, more real. It wouldn't sound just like pipe-dreaming when I discussed my career with Miss Goodfellow in our conversation breaks.

*

The following Saturday at Grandma's, when everyone had finished eating, and in the hope that my announcement would be greeted with cries of approval, I said: 'I'm going to be an artist.'

'Shut up!' Grandma cried instantly, as if I had said a dirty word.

'You don't know what you're talking about,' my father snapped.

'No, really!' I insisted, avoiding my mother's eyes. 'It's the only thing I want to do.'

'You'll starve to death,' Grandma cried. 'Artist.' She shuddered, throwing a piece of herring into her mouth.

'You'll be working for me,' my father said quietly. I shot a look at my mother but her face said very clearly, 'I told you not to breathe a word of this. Now you have, you're on your own.'

Grandpa remained silent. I knew he didn't approve but surely he would help me out?

'Grandpa?' I prompted him.

He gazed at me thoughtfully. 'The last artist in this family was me, and I nearly starved,' he pointed out. 'The Paris Opera paid the lowest salaries ...'

'Yeah, artist!' Grandma said scornfully. 'I'd like to see what we'd be eating today if you'd stayed a' artist. Not smoked salmon, that's for sure.' To underline her point, she dug up a strip of smoked salmon and dangled it into her mouth.

'Darling, when you choose a profession,' Grandpa explained, 'you must choose one that can support a family. You expect to have a family, don't you?'

Everyone looked at me. 'No,' I said, surprising even myself. I suddenly realised that I must suffer alone for my art, like Miss Goodfellow.

'You don't want a *family*?' Grandma cried.

I shook my head. 'Van Gogh never had children,' I informed her. 'Neither did Toulouse Lautrec.'

'Are they Jewish?' Grandma asked angrily. 'Because most Jewish people want families. You're going to give me great-grandchildren, aren't you? I expect at least three from each of you.'

'Well, that's too bad, Grandma, because I don't intend to have any,' I retorted.

'Don't you *dare* answer back to your grandmother!' Dad exploded. 'You'll be joining me in the factory when you leave school. Making handbags and selling them to the finest stores in London. You're damn lucky you have a job waiting for you.'

'But I want to be an artist,' I said, trying to sound forceful. 'Surely I can decide for myself what work I do?'

'Drawing pictures isn't work,' Dad pronounced.

'Oh? This isn't work?' I asked, hunting for my sketch-book, which I kept nearby in case someone slumped into an interesting pose. I flicked through the sketches I had done recently of friends and family.

'You think artists don't work?' I asked, my voice breaking. 'I bet I'd be working harder than you.'

Quick as a flash, my father slapped my face, hard. He grabbed my sketchbook and ripped some pages from it, crumpling them into a ball. I glared at him, stunned, my cheek burning with the sting. There was complete silence in the kitchen. My eyes filled with tears but I knew I must not let one spill, not in front of everyone. I bit my lower lip and tried not to blink.

'You shouldn't have spoiled his drawings,' my mother murmured.

An artist doesn't cry, I told myself. He pours his intense feelings into his work. My father glared back at me. He did not like my questioning how hard he worked – it was his Achilles heel. I felt young, powerless and inadequate. How many years must pass before I upped and left this family, even if it meant leaving my mother?

'Why don't you children go and play some records?' Grandpa suggested.

We all jumped to our feet. As we passed Grandma she reached out and pulled me to her, staring straight into my eyes, her scarlet lipstick slashed across her mouth, her eyes glinting green. 'I'll give you artist,' she threatened, and let go.

In the small sitting room, we played American 78s on the huge radiogram. My brain was racing.

'Not so funny when you're suddenly not the favourite, is it?' Rachel gloated. 'Now you know how I felt when he told me I was fat.'

'I'd like to kill him,' I muttered.

'Ha!' She twirled her full skirt in time to the beat of the Four Aces. 'Let me know if you think of a way.'

Nothing was said about the incident on the drive home that night, but a new core of hate was burning inside me, like a steady flame. Hate for my father. His silence as he drove was threatening, but I refused to be threatened. I would let him believe I was joining him in his stinking factory, it would give me time to plan my escape. He had never talked to me of a 'future' in handbags, never attempted to make the business sound interesting to a small boy. The designing, the production, the acquisition of beautiful leathers, the sales – they could have been made to sound interesting, exciting even. I was more angry at his not bothering to involve me in the business than at his standing in the way of my career as an artist. The slap in front of my grandparents and the destruction of my sketches had demolished whatever love for him there might have been in me, and now I realised that there had never really been any. This new knowledge that I did not love my father was strangely liberating and strengthening. A weight of pretence had slipped from my shoulders.

My mother had sometimes pointed out a man in the street, a large ugly man who always studiedly ignored us as we passed him. 'See him?' she would whisper, nudging me. 'See that man? That man was nearly your father.' She had said this since I was too young to understand, and I used to stare after the man, imagining some mail-order catalogue of fathers from which she had nearly ordered this one.

'I almost got engaged to him before I met Dad,' she explained when I looked puzzled. 'If I'd married him, he would have been your father.' I felt a shiver of strangeness, gazing after the retreating almost-Dad, wondering if I would have preferred him.

Now I felt that I would have preferred any other man, any father I could have discussed things with, any father who would have listened to me. We could have argued about his idea that enjoyable work didn't count as work. Although Dad had never mentioned the factory in terms other than an aggravating duty he was obliged to do, a chore that gave him stomach ulcers, I knew from talking with friends that some fathers liked their work. There were lawyers, doctors, even shopgirls and cleaners, who did not all see work as a loathsome chore.

Mum crept into my bedroom later that night, holding some pieces of paper. 'Here, darling.' She proudly handed them to me. 'I ironed them out and they're as good as new.'

I took them from her, frowning. She had picked up the creased sketches from Grandma's kitchen floor and ironed them. I stared at this evidence of her magic.

'Oh, thanks, Mum.' I stood up to hug her. 'I hate him, you know,' I said casually as I broke away.

She smiled, shaking her head. 'Of course you don't,' she

said. 'He's your father. How could a son hate his own father?'

'How?' I echoed her innocent question. 'He just has to have a father like mine, that's how.' I wanted to say so much more. That it wasn't only me, we all hated him. But I didn't want to hurt her. One mother like her was worth a million fathers like him.

*

Icily polite. That was my new way to handle Dad.

He didn't notice. As long as we washed the car on Sundays, said 'Good morning' daily, did not spill orange squash or ask for money, he was fairly normal. But I was frightened of him; frightened that he might have the power to make me work in his factory. If I ran away, would I qualify for state aid? Could I perhaps win a scholarship to some art school, could I get a grant? I had to find out about the outside world and the rights and allowances of a young man without parental support.

I drew constantly, hoping that it would ensure my being an artist. For fifteen minutes a day my mother was my captive model. We had no maid at the time and in the late afternoons, after she had scoured the house from top to bottom, Mum would take a scalding bath, filling the upper landing with pine-scented steam. She would relax on my bed, rolled in a huge white bath towel and towelled turban. I considered it a great honour that she chose my bed. Each day, as she dozed, biblical in her turban, I would draw her horizontal profile against the light from the window. There was a small birthmark in the centre of her forehead like the red powdered mark of a Hindu on a festival day, turning her into an exotic Indian princess.

*

By the time I was thirteen and a half, there were still no signs of my long-awaited adolescence. I began to search library files for books on 'late' or 'delayed' puberty.

Surprisingly, there was not one book on this life-or-death subject. I considered seeing Dr Kossoff to ask whether there was something wrong with me, but I could not face asking him such intimate questions. He might ask me to undress and start prodding me. I read that the latest recorded case of puberty starting had been that of an Indian boy of twenty-two. Was I going to break the record?

A little later a new self-consciousness had me deciding, several hours in advance, what to do with my hands upon entering a room. Whichever way I let them hang, they felt and looked wrong. I tried out postures before the bathroom mirror. I felt everyone was looking at me. This was awkwardness! This was adolescence! Then I found a cache of pornographic magazines in a brown envelope left by some pervert in a telephone box. He obviously meant them to be recycled, so I took immediate possession. The collection of nudist, pin-up and fetishist magazines pushed me into the solitary sexual pleasures I had seen demonstrated behind the school cycle-sheds. I was no longer a little boy.

7

Bringing Art to the Family

'Your father says you must *work* for a living,' Grandma greeted me as she opened her front door the week after my announcement.

I was visiting her alone on a weekday after school, as part of a public relations exercise to acquaint my family with what an artist did. Perhaps if they understood the work involved, some of the mistrust and fear would melt?

'Yes. Your father thinks you should *work*,' Grandma repeated, leading the way back to the kitchen. 'Like everyone else has to.'

I was pleased she was alone; it would make my job a little easier if she had no audience to play to. If I could get her on my side, the rest of the family would be bound to follow. She gave me a brief kiss with no hug, to show that she was vaguely displeased, and began to scrub the immaculate white tiles behind her kitchen sink, as if to underline her point about work.

'I thought I'd tell you how an artist works, Grandma,' I began, sitting down. 'An artist works longer hours than anyone. He's always looking at things, memorising them, sketching them. An artist works day and night.' I rummaged in my satchel for sketchbook and pencil.

'Oh yes?' Grandma peeled off her pink rubber gloves with a snap. 'I don't see *you* working day and night. Why aren't you working right now? It's still day, isn't it?'

'I'm going to draw you,' I said, turning to a fresh page.

'You're just trying to win me round,' she decided, reaching for the kettle and filling it. 'So as I'll talk your father into letting you off working in the factory. But 'e'll

never agree to you bein' no artist. We've never 'ad no artist
in our family and we don't need one now, thank you.' She
banged the kettle down onto the flame.

'But Grandpa was an artist,' I said.

'What are you talking about, *what* artist?' she cried.

'He sang, didn't he? In the Paris Opera?'

Grandma laughed. 'Oh, 'e sang, all right. 'E sang a lot, 'e
did. And 'ow much money d'you think 'e made out of it?
Enough to marry and have children? Do me a favour.'

'Well, did he sing at the Paris Opera or didn't he?' I
asked.

She stared at me. 'If 'e says 'e sang there, it must be
true,' she said. 'You don't want me to make out your grandfather for a liar, do you?'

'I'd just like to know the real story,' I replied.

'Real story, ha!' Grandma sneered. 'The real story is
that if 'e were singin' at the Paris Opera, we'd 'ave all
starved to death, that's the real story.' She arranged the
cups noisily, shooting a look at my sketchbook. 'And I
don't call *that* work,' she added, as I began to draw her.

'Okay, Grandma, but try to keep still and tell me what
you consider work?' I said. 'Digging for coal down the
mines? Prisoners on a chain gang, manacled to each
other?'

'*What* manacle, what are you talking about?' she said
impatiently. She set the cups down before us and sat stirring her tea. 'Are you still drawing me?' she asked, sitting
up impossibly straight, then immediately beginning to sag.
I began again, now that she was sitting down. 'I 'ope you're
givin' that to me,' she said.

'If you'd like it,' I said casually, trying not to exaggerate
the disproportionate amount of space her nose took up on
her face. Without make-up, the scarlet slash of her mouth did
not detract attention from it, so that one saw only the nose.

'Yes, I'll 'ave it,' Grandma said. 'And when you've
finished me, you can do your grandfather. 'E's asleep.' She
indicated the bedroom. ''E won't move.'

I was pleased she wasn't wearing her usual white gloves;
I could make a feature of her long dark nails. Grandma

froze, regally, as I added some professional-seeming shading. When it was finished I tore out the page and presented it to her.

'Hmmmm …' She held it this way and that, squinting. 'It looks a *bit* like me, but this only took you five minutes. I thought you said you'd be working day and night. What would you get for this – if you sold it?'

'Er … fifty pounds?' I said, wildly overvaluing my work to impress her.

She gasped. 'I wouldn't give no fifty pounds for *this*,' she laughed. But she placed it carefully on the sideboard, adding, 'I'm keeping it.'

'It could be worth more one day,' I told her. 'If I became well known.'

'And 'ow d'you become well known?' she asked.

I sat back, savouring the question. It was so rare for Grandma to ask me one. It meant admitting she didn't know the answer. I leaned my chin on my fist, thoughtfully.

'I'd need a gallery to exhibit my work. They'd invite art critics. If they liked it, collectors would want to buy my paintings. Little by little, I'd get well known.'

Grandma stared at the portrait for a moment, then snorted 'Humph!' She finished her tea, giving me a little smile. 'You're the only one of my grandchildren who visits me,' she said. 'Nice of you to come and see your old Grandma. I was a bit lonely. Your grandfather would sleep all day if I let 'im. Go an' draw '*im*! '*E* won't move.'

I did not want to draw my sleeping grandfather but if I refused it would prove Grandma's theory that artists were layabouts, so I went off in search of my next model.

Grandpa lay asleep on the bed with its headboard of tufted white satin. He wore trousers and a white, sleeveless vest. The quilted white satin bedspread had been carefully folded to one side. The curtains were drawn, the dim room filled with his cologned smell and soft snoring. I perched on the satin-covered dressing-table stool and began to draw. It felt eerie, an intrusion of his privacy, and the resulting 'Portrait of Sleeping Grandfather' did not do him justice. I had not reckoned with closed eyes closing off a large chunk of the subject's personality, or that a horizontal, creased, sleeping face was harder to capture than an awake, up-and-down face. I finished it off hastily, not wanting Grandpa to awake and get a fright when he saw me sitting there. I showed the drawing to Grandma and left soon after, unsure whether my visit had done my cause any good.

'You're crazy to think you could earn a decent living with this!' she called after me, waving the portraits.

She was frightened of anything new, anything different, I thought on the bus home. I didn't understand that her insecure childhood had caused this, I thought it was just how old people reasoned. Not only distrusting the new, she mocked anything outside her experience; people prepared to risk it were fools. Well, I was prepared to risk it, in spite of her warning.

*

'Lovely little *schluff*.' Grandpa yawned, stretching his arms as we left the flea-pit cinema the following Saturday. 'You can only get that kind of *schluff* in a cinema.'

'Waste of a cinema seat,' I complained. We had sat through a double bill of Doris Day musicals and I felt a little sick, as if I'd been force-fed too much Technicolor syrup. Doris Day was just supportable, but her male partners – Gordon MacRae and Gene Nelson – were too bland for my taste.

Grandpa blinked in the Edgware Road sunlight, yawning again. 'Why are you always so tired, Grandpa?' I asked.

He took my arm, chuckling. 'You don't *schluff* because you're tired,' he tried to explain. 'It's more a question of relaxing. Sleep is a natural cure.'

We headed towards my favourite milk-bar, the Black and White. Tiled with rather shabby black and white tiles, it did pretty good milk-shakes.

'Did you sleep a lot when you were in the Paris Opera?' I questioned.

'More than now,' Grandpa nodded. 'Twenty hours a day,

sometimes. Got up, went to the Opera, did my bit, came straight home to bed.'

'Wasn't it a waste of time?'

We entered the café. 'Not when you're cold and hungry,' Grandpa said quietly. We sat at a table and Grandpa wiped the wet top with a paper napkin. 'What are you going to have?'

'A vanilla milk-shake, please.'

I felt slightly ashamed, not knowing what to say about his cold, hungry, Paris youth. It only came up when I questioned him, unlike my father's youth which he was always throwing up at us to show us how lucky we were.

The waitress approached. 'The young man will have a vanilla milk-shake, and I'll take a black coffee and a doughnut,' Grandpa ordered.

'I bumped into Aunt Hilda last week,' I said.

'Oh yes? How is she?' he asked.

'She's not my aunt,' I found myself saying.

He glanced at me. 'You call some ladies "Auntie" don't you?' he said calmly. 'Your neighbours, your mother's friends?'

'Yes, but –' I frowned.

'You're thirteen, surely you know who your real family is by now?' he asked.

Our orders arrived and Grandpa bit into his doughnut, making a red blob of jam appear. I sipped my shake.

'She's upset about Christine,' I said.

'Who's Christine?' Grandpa faked surprise.

'The girl you sent Jack to New York to get out of his system, Grandpa,' I reminded him.

Grandpa gave me a cagey look. 'What are you, a detective?' he growled. He finished his coffee and signalled the waitress for another.

'Hilda says Jack's the only man in the world for Christine,' I said. 'And she's the only girl for Jack. It's like Romeo and Juliet.'

'Is it?' Grandpa said glumly. His second coffee arrived and he stirred sugar into it.

'You do remember Romeo and Juliet?' I prompted him.

'They were personal friends of mine,' Grandpa said.

'Please, Grandpa, don't always joke,' I complained. 'Are you against them marrying? As much as Grandma is?'

He tapped his pockets. 'I could use a cigar,' he said. 'Left 'em at home.' As he continued to stir his coffee, I could see he was tempted to talk. Perhaps even confide in me.

'Look, we're not such strict Jews, are we?' he asked me. 'Would we be watching pictures on *shabbos*, handling money and all the rest of it?' He jingled the loose change in his pockets. Religious Jews could not touch money on Saturdays. 'Religion?' He gave a slow shrug. I felt the tingling thrill of adulthood, of being treated as an equal by my grandfather. 'I don't believe in it.' Grandpa looked me in the eyes. 'If you want to know the truth.'

'Nor do *I*,' I burst out. 'Dad always says it's a lot of baloney. My rabbi told me Adam and Eve were fish.'

'Fish?' Grandpa frowned. 'What kind of nonsense is that?'

'I know.' I beamed. 'So why don't you believe?' This would be a red-letter day. I had never expected to be discussing religion with Grandpa.

'Why don't I believe?' Grandpa repeated thoughtfully, sipping his coffee.

I waited. Had no one asked him this question before? He looked up and I saw his eyes were full of tears.

'If you'd seen what I saw during the war, darling.' He fumbled for his large white handkerchief. 'The families, the children … torn apart, lost …' He blew his nose. 'You wouldn't need to ask me why I don't believe,' he ended gruffly.

I reached out to touch his hand. 'I'm sorry, Grandpa,' I said. 'I didn't mean to upset you.'

This was why we never discussed religion, wars or politics in our family. Someone always started crying, as if it were too painful to talk about. The tears suggested horrors beyond our imagination.

'I'm not very religious, but I'm still a Jew,' Grandpa said, suddenly thumping the table. 'It's natural that my wife wants her son to marry a Jewish girl.'

'And you go along with it to keep Grandma quiet?' I asked.

Grandpa stuffed the handkerchief back into his pocket. 'I paid a very expensive air fare to New York to keep Grandma quiet,' he chuckled. 'Are you finished?'

I tried to get the last drops through my straw without making any noise. 'What d'you think will happen?' I asked him. He searched in his jacket pocket for change.

'*Que sera, sera*,' he shrugged. He must have noticed my disappointed face because he shot me an exasperated look. 'Darling, there are problems with a mixed marriage,' he pointed out. 'The children, the in-laws, all that. And I feel quite a bit to blame for all this.'

'Why?'

'Because he met Christine through me,' he confessed. 'How else do you think he'd meet a *shiksa*? He doesn't just talk to girls on the street. You can't imagine how your grandmother protected him. You know he didn't know what night was until he was fourteen?' I nodded, smiling. 'I didn't expect them to want to marry each other, believe me,' he said, folding his serviette. 'I've been like an uncle to Christine. I knew her father – nice fellow – used to work in the factory for us. Then her mother died, the father moved to Brighton and Christine came to live with Hilda. I'm walking with your Uncle Jack one day – this was years ago – and we bump into Hilda with Christine. It would have been bad manners not to offer them a drink. We had sherry in a pub. Those two young ones stared at each other, too shy to say a word. Did I know they'd fall in love? To me, she was a child.' He signalled the waitress for the bill. 'I just didn't think Jack would be so ready to settle down with the first girl he met. I offered him a Jaguar to give her up – you saw what happened. He couldn't eat, he couldn't sleep, could I torture my own son? He has his life to live too!'

'Poor Grandpa,' I said.

'So we thought a year apart might be a good thing,' he said. 'Let him meet other girls, let her meet other boys …'

'But she's not meeting other boys,' I told him.

'No?' He raised his eyebrows. 'Well, I'm sure Jack's

meeting other girls. Frankie will see to it.' He stared mean-ingfully at me.

The waitress took his money and gave him the change on a saucer. Grandpa stood up and buttoned his coat. He left a shilling. As we walked up the Edgware Road, he said, 'The funny thing about all this is that Christine is a lovely girl. Sweet, kind, bright – she got all her GCEs. She's better educated than Jack, you know. Your grandmother may just have to get used to the idea.'

'And their children?' I asked, walking along beside him.

'Listen.' Grandpa nudged me. 'When your grandmother sees a new grandchild, she'll love it even if it's Chinese!'

*

Four months later, Uncle Jack came home for a week. He said it was because he missed his mother, but I guessed that Christine was the real reason. Without alerting his parents, he simply arrived at the West London Air Terminal, took a bus to Marble Arch and lugged his heavy suitcase to the flat. Early one Saturday morning, Grandma's neighbours ran towards the screams of what sounded like a woman being attacked, but it was only Grandma's surprise and delight at being reunited with Jack. She was so happy that she overlooked the fact that the reason for his return was probably the same reason he had been sent to New York to forget.

Uncle Jack brought us boxes of bubble-gum, clockwork toys, pencil-sharpeners in the shape of pianos and armchairs, comics and candy. These became my most trea-sured possessions. The smell of America – which for me was a mixture of Lifesavers, Fleer's Dubble-Bubble and comic-newsprint – was a drug I inhaled several times a day. It represented glamour, hope and excitement and I dreamed of visiting or even living in America one day.

Jack also brought glossy menus from coffee shops and restaurants. We pored over the extraordinary items: twenty-seven varieties of 'foot-long hot-dogs'; Submarines; Torpedoes, and Poor Boys, which Uncle Jack said were just snappy names for cheese rolls. They certainly didn't look like cheese rolls in the colourful illustrations. Surrounded by pickles, salad, relish and potato-chips, they resembled a feast.

'You can live off the garnish in New York,' Jack said as we marvelled. 'Before you even order anything they put a bowl of dill pickles on the table, crackers, butter-pats, jugs of iced water. Bums come in off the street' – we giggled at the rude word – 'and eat crackers and butter and pickles, drink the water and leave without paying a cent.'

I noted that New York might be a good place for a starving artist. Uncle Jack said he had seen a man trying to gulp hot soup throwing ice cubes into it to cool it down. New Yorkers were so rushed that they ate salad, using plastic forks, as they ran down the sidewalk. The crowd on Fifth Avenue sometimes walked so fast that you could get caught up and swept in the wrong direction. It all made up a picture of American life that we added to the comics, the television series like *I Love Lucy* or *Dragnet*, the gum-wrappers and the movies, to create a funny, crazy world.

We thought the menus had been brought back to amuse us, but the evening of Jack's return saw the grown-ups examining them closely and beginning to scheme. What was to stop someone introducing this exciting new cheap food to England? they wondered. Would this not make a fortune for the people clever enough to promote it? What, Jack argued, did the poor British public have? If you were rich you could dine at Wheeler's, or Simpson's, or the Ritz. Otherwise, there were Quality Inns, Forte's Milk Bars, fish and chip shops or Chinese restaurants where they surely used cat-food.

'I wouldn't eat in any of them places if you *paid* me,' Grandma began to scream. 'They've all got rats!'

'I was sick the last time I ate in a Chinese restaurant,' my mother said, giving me a dark look.

'The waiters go to the lavatory and don't wash their hands,' Grandma shuddered.

I half listened to all this without taking it in. The grown-ups were always discussing new ways to make money, yet our lives never changed. I did not connect this scheming to my ambitions of becoming an artist. I did not realise that if the factory were sold, I would be free.

8

The Brothers' Return

That year's summer holidays began differently. I had lost interest in my studies and my marks had suffered. When I picked up my end-of-year report from the master's desk on the last afternoon of term, I saw that I had tumbled spectacularly. From being amongst the top ten boys of the class, I was now in the bottom ten. My teachers competed to find the most disappointed adjective for their summing-up of my progress. 'Inexplicable' was the favourite. I couldn't explain it either. I walked home that afternoon very slowly, praying for a miracle. Perhaps Dad would forget to ask for the report.

We were not going to the seaside that year as the house was being repaired and repainted. Ursula had left us so I no longer had her barefooted support. We were back to Irish girls who didn't know Dali from Van Gogh and showed no interest in my sketchbook even when I left it lying about, open. That evening, my father's hand emerged as usual from behind his paper and his fingers clicked for the report. Feeling sick, I passed it to him. He took a long time reading it.

'If this is the best you can do, you may as well leave school early and come to work for me,' he said.

I slunk off to my room, smarting with the shock of no longer being a genius. I hadn't appreciated the way Dad had said 'working for me', as if it would be a punishment.

My usually pleasurable holidays turned into hot empty days with the threat that had been so casually thrown out by my father hanging over them. Books lost their fascination and the piano seemed sticky and tuneless. School pals sometimes telephoned to suggest an outing, but I preferred my own little world of Freud, films and art.

The only encouraging person around was Miss Goodfellow. At times, when I wavered in my career choice of artist, I would try alternative career choices out on her. She pronounced my latest idea of night-club pianist 'jolly good'. I stood for long periods before the bathroom mirror, hoping it would reflect back a sophisticated enter-tainer, but I saw only an overweight, spotty boy. I should have been swimming, cycling or at least reading outdoors, but instead I gorged myself on Kit Kats and Slams, stayed in and read film magazines' advice to Debbie Reynolds on how to win back Eddie Fisher from Liz Taylor.

One morning, at the end of August, my mother woke me by running into my room and sitting down at the end of my bed.

'The brothers are coming home!' she cried. I tried to focus on her, rubbing the sleep from my eyes. It was half past eight and I could hear the sound of the gardener mowing the lawn outside. 'They just called from New York,' Mum said, her eyes sparkling. 'They'll be on the boat this afternoon and they arrive in Southampton on Saturday.' I sat up in bed; I loved seeing her this happy.

'You'll get to know your Uncle Frankie – he's a wonderful man,' she continued, 'and you'll have a brand-new American aunt – Auntie Joyce. And your little cousin Barbara is adorable. So grown-up. When we visited New York two years ago, she was just two years old. I had a headache one evening and you know what that child did? She ran to the bathroom and came back with two aspirin in her hand.'

'Sounds a bit precocious,' I yawned. I clasped my mother's hands. 'I'm glad you're happy, Mum. What's Auntie Joyce like?'

'Well, it's hard to tell with Americans.' My mother made a face. 'They're always so friendly. She seems very nice. To your face. I don't think she likes anybody very much. She brings up Barbara nicely, dresses her beautifully, but why not? She spends all her time shopping. Barbara can be a little sister for Rachel, she's always wanted one.'

At dinner that night, Mum couldn't stop talking about her brothers' return. Dad didn't seem quite so interested.

'Grandma will be a different person,' Mum predicted. 'She loves her sons much more than she loves me.'

I wondered how she could say it so matter-of-factly.

'She'll start her Friday night dinners again for all the family – in the dining room, the kitchen isn't good enough for her Frankie. Wait till you taste how your Grandma cooks for her sons!'

'Does she like Auntie Joyce?' Rachel asked.

Mum glanced over at my father and laughed. 'Could she like any woman who stole one of her precious sons?' she asked.

'She likes Dad,' Rachel said.

'Yes, because he took me off her hands,' Mum said. 'It's different with sons.' She shot me a quick look.

'We'll drive down to Southampton with Grandma and Grandpa to meet the boat,' my father told us. 'You'd think two conquering heroes were returning instead of two *pishers* who couldn't make it in America.' (*Pisher*, literally 'little pisser' was his strongest insult.)

'Don't call them that!' Mum cried. 'Frankie's done very well there. They have so much luggage they'll need two cars. It'll be a lovely outing.'

The following Saturday we rose at five-thirty for the drive. We formed a convoy of two with Dad in his emerald-green 'Henry J' and Grandpa in his steel-grey Triumph. Rachel travelled with my grandparents. I knelt on the back seat, waving at them as they followed us. Grandma's hair shone like candy-floss. She had a new 'dream come true' expression of dazed wonderment and weepy ecstasy. There had been no time to worry, she had been so busy cooking. She motioned to me to turn around and keep my eye on the road.

It took hours to reach Southampton. No one in the family had a sense of direction, nor could we follow directions if we stopped to ask the way. No one could read a map. The ship had docked by the time we found it, passengers streaming down the gangway into the crowds of welcomers. We pressed into this mob, Grandma clutching Grandpa's arm. At ten-thirty in the morning, she seemed even more clownish, face powdered dead white, mouth a slash of crimson. The lips turned down as she relived the years without her sons, then turned up as she remembered they were about to reappear. She looked like alternate masks of comedy or tragedy, depending on which bit she was thinking of.

A family near us spotted someone and Grandma got swept into their excitement as they embraced an elderly man. She wept alongside them and Grandpa had to hold her back when she seemed about to embrace the man herself. Dabbing her cheeks with a hanky, her red eyes caught mine. 'I can't 'elp it,' she confessed. She sometimes went to airports or railway stations just to watch family reunions, weeping and laughing as if they were her family.

'Oh my God, I think that's Frankie!' my mother suddenly cried. 'He's got Barbara on his shoulders. Look!'

Grandma let out a shrill scream.

A little girl in bright yellow was perching on the shoulders of a round-faced, balding man. He waved, 'Hey, Ma!' The little girl, who looked as if she'd stepped straight out of our 'Little Lulu' comics, cried, 'Grandma?'

'I'm going to faint!' Grandma cried, but her arms went straight out before her and she suddenly became a life-sized statue symbolising 'Welcome'. When her sons and my aunt reached her, she flew into action, demonstrating her ability to embrace four people simultaneously. She delivered her famous flurries of kisses, a couple of dozen quickly plonked in succession over every available surface of face, head and neck. It was an unforgettable display of love. We waited patiently. Now and then Grandma released a son to clutch at her heart, as if to forestall a funny turn. But she soon returned to the hard work of welcoming home a family. She pulled her granddaughter from her father's shoulders and smothered her face in kisses, growling, 'Ooooh, I could eat her up.' It would have frightened any other child, but not a native New Yorker. At three and a half, Barbara had a quicker wit and wider vocabulary than any of us. She simply giggled.

As I waited my turn to greet her, I studied Auntie Joyce. She did not disappoint me. If Barbara was from 'Little Lulu', Joyce was *I Love Lucy*, complete with bright orange lips pencilled in way outside their natural outlines. Her waved hair was Technicolor yellow, a colour that did not even try to be natural. Her turquoise twin-set over a pencil-slim navy skirt was worn with lots of chunky gold jewellery – false too, surely. The idea of so much of Joyce – lips, hair, jewels – being frankly false was exciting. It qualified her to join my collection of female eccentrics.

'So *this* is Howard?' her warm, breathy American voice purred in my ear. She stared at me through narrow tortoiseshell spectacles, their lenses tinted a mysterious pale blue. She leaned to peck my cheek. I felt as if I had been swept into a Hollywood movie. 'You play piano, you love movies and you're very artistic,' she listed. 'See? I know all about you. I *am* going to hear you play?'

I nodded, struck dumb for a moment, falling in love with the idea of an American aunt.

'Barbara's just longing to meet you,' she said. 'Come, say hello to your new cousin.'

My uncles gave me manly handshakes and pats on the shoulder. I only vaguely remembered Uncle Frankie – he had got older, fatter and balder. Jack had lost his gloomy air and was smiling and lively; America had been good for him. Uncle Frankie hugged and kissed everyone, laughed away Grandma's tears and placed a protective arm around Grandpa, whom he resembled. His balding head shone, his cheeks were flushed and his big brown eyes darted here and there, watching for his luggage. When it arrived, piled high on a huge trolley, he swept up his daughter with one hand and shepherded the group and the porter towards the Customs shed.

'Oh, my God, *Customs*!' Grandma cried, eyes wide with alarm. 'Don't declare anything. Say that everything's used or second-hand. You'll pay a fortune in duty, otherwise.' She pulled at Joyce's arm in her panic.

Joyce coolly disengaged herself.

'I have an American passport, Mom,' she announced.

'I've a perfect right to bring my possessions into this country.'

Grandma dropped her arm in surprise. Joyce, Frankie and Jack walked fearlessly into the shed, leaving us to wait by the large sliding doors. When they emerged, twenty minutes later, Grandma seemed quite disappointed that they hadn't had to pay any duty.

When we reached the cars, Lawrence and I begged to have our new cousin with us. Joyce placed Barbara on the back seat and she stretched her little legs before her. '*Now* where are we going?' she sighed.

'To London, honey,' Joyce told her.

Rachel joined the uncles in Grandpa's car and we all became part of the long line of cars snaking towards the exit.

'I saw a terrific movie in New York just before we left, Howard,' Joyce told me. '*The King and I*, with Deborah Kerr and that bald guy. He shaves his head, you know. And she doesn't really sing – they dubbed in a better voice.'

I nodded. 'I have the piano selection.' Was I really going to have someone in the family to discuss films with?

We peered into Grandpa's car as we overtook them. The uncles were talking away, Grandma still dabbing her tears of joy. Aunt Joyce's knowing eyes gleamed amusedly from behind the powerful tinted lenses. She waved several times before realising that her husband was unaware of her. I felt slightly sorry for her as she turned her head to face the front. She had had Frankie to herself for six years, and now she would be sharing him with his mother. She seemed reconciled to this. I liked my eccentric females to be slightly tragic so I decided that she was in London against her will. I overlooked her heavy legs and strangely placid air. I liked her and wanted her to like me.

'I can't wait to hit your stores, Sis,' she leaned forward to tell my mother.

'Hit them?' Mum laughed. 'What are you going to hit them with?'

'No, I mean shop,' Joyce explained as everyone laughed. I wondered why Mum didn't seem to like her very much.

('How can you like someone who doesn't drink or smoke?'
she offered later when I tackled her. 'You can't relax with
them over a cigarette or a cocktail.' I didn't understand. I
preferred people who didn't drink or smoke.) I felt a rush
of injustice on Joyce's behalf and vowed to be especially
nice to her. I appreciated the way she spoke to me as an
equal and only noticed much later that she spoke to babies
and dogs as if they were complete equals too. I plied her
with questions about New York. When we reached the
outskirts of London, she squinted through the windows at
the grey streets.

'Gee,' she said. 'London is … a shock!'

'They've rented a lovely house for you,' my mother
twisted in her seat to tell her. 'It's ten minutes from us by
car, an area called Brondesbury. Quiet, mostly Jewish. If
you like it, the owners might sell. It's got a lovely garden.'

'And lots of storage too, I hope?' Joyce asked. 'I kinda
got used to those huge New York walk-in closets. It's just
that we have so much stuff. The sales there are so great you
feel stupid if you *don't* buy. We have towels and blankets
and sheets in all colours of the rainbow.'

I stared at her enviously. We didn't have a towel that
wasn't white or a blanket that wasn't pale blue. I hadn't
known that you could get them in any other colours.

Outside Grandma's flat, Uncle Frankie decided that it
wasn't worth *schlepping* all their luggage up to the flat. My
father agreed to drive them to their house, drop off the
luggage and bring them back for lunch. It was after one
and we were starving.

'I could eat,' Joyce kept saying. I found that odd.
Grandma did too.

'Did you 'ear 'er?' she asked my mother as my father
drove them away. 'She "*could*" eat! 'Ere I've been cooking
for three days and she's going to force 'erself to eat.' She
began climbing the stairs to the flat. 'And I'll bet she isn't
even wearing a corset.'

My mother, following her, laughed. 'Oh, Ma, lots of
women don't feel they need them these days.'

Grandma turned to give her a look. '*She* needs one.'

Rachel and I exchanged glances.

Upstairs, Grandma removed her coat and dress and donned a big white apron. I helped Uncle Jack lug his heavy bags into his old room.

'How does it feel to be back?' I asked him shyly, as he searched for the keys to his locks.

'Okay,' he shrugged, snapping open his case. Without his brother around, he had reverted to dull old gloomy Jack. I didn't dare mention Christine, but I imagined he couldn't wait to see her.

In the kitchen Grandma was stirring a huge cauldron of chicken soup with dozens of pale *kneidlach* floating on top. 'Who's gonna eat all this food, Ma?' Jack grumbled, coming in. 'They stuffed us like turkeys on the ship.'

'They'll eat,' Grandma prophesised grimly. 'They don't serve food like this on no ship. Three days, this chicken has been simmering.'

Her cooking could usually be read as some kind of code signalling how much she loved or valued the family or friends partaking of the meal. No dish demanded more sacrifice than her famous three-day *gedempt* chicken, if only for the 72-hour watch over the tiny light, so low it was in danger of getting snuffed out if someone walked quickly past the stove. That and very gentle stirring ensured that the meat fell off the bone as you placed it on your tongue. In less masterful hands, such chicken can get overcooked, losing all flavour. In Grandma's case, the orgy of simmering somehow released flavours that even the chicken didn't know it possessed. It became concentrated, the very essence of chicken, and it did literally melt over the taste-buds and into the mouth.

We carried stacks of white plates and bowls down the corridor into the dining room. Grandpa hovered near the table, seeming quieter than usual.

'Why don't you have a little *schluff*, Dad?' my mother suggested, peering at him. 'Take forty winks, go on! They'll be a while yet.'

He didn't need much urging and was soon snoring quietly in his corner armchair as everyone bustled silently around him, adding thick glass tumblers to the table and big white soft napkins to each place-setting.

'My Frankie's got big ideas,' Grandma said to my mother in the kitchen, gently stirring the soup. 'Wants to see us all get out of handbags into catering. As if I don't do enough cooking, day in, day out.'

'Are you pleased to have them back, Grandma?' I asked.

'No! I wish they'd go back tomorrow,' she snapped at me. 'What a question! Of *course* I'm pleased. What mother likes 'er children to live on the other side of the world? This'll give your grandfather a new lease of life, 'e's missed 'is sons.' I glanced quickly at my mother, but she was so happy to have her brothers back that she did not register the dig.

It was three o'clock by the time Frankie and Joyce returned and our stomachs were grumbling. Grandpa was woken and bowls of steaming soup carried very carefully, two by two, down the corridor. First the men were served, then the children, and, finally, the women. Grandma's chicken soup did have magical qualities, awakening the appetite even of those who swore they weren't hungry: they all requested second helpings. The *kneidlach* were feather-light and delicious.

Joyce, who had quickly taken to calling Grandma 'Mom', called out: 'Oh, and I'll have a few more dumplings, please.'

'I'm not counting,' Grandma growled in the kitchen, 'but she's eaten *fourteen kneidlach*! Don't tell me you can eat fourteen *kneidlach* if you're wearing a corset.'

I helped take in the soup. Everyone was talking, the brothers talking big.

'Yes, the British public will be able to eat something tasty at last, without spending a lot of money,' Frankie was saying. 'And we'll make a fortune. You know why?'

My father shrugged.

'Because we'll have no competition,' Frankie said simply, spreading his hands wide.

I knew instinctively that he was using the wrong tone, explaining things to my father as if he were an idiot.

'Did you make a fortune in New York?' my father asked. He was starting to get irritated at all this sales talk and wanted to be allowed to enjoy his meal in peace.

'A few million fellows got there ahead of me,' Frankie smiled. 'I looked around to see what I could learn there to apply here. And each time I looked I came up with the same answer – food.'

Grandma brought in a platter of roast chicken, roast potatoes and peas.

'People will always need to eat,' Jack said solemnly. 'Three times a day. That's a thousand times a year.'

'How many times a year does a woman need to buy a handbag?' Frankie asked my father.

My father considered this. 'No one ever said you'd die if you didn't buy a new handbag,' he said quietly. 'It's a luxury item.'

'Don't compare handbags to food,' Grandpa suddenly growled.

'Handbags are a limited market, Pa, that's all I'm saying,' Frankie placated him. 'When you design a handbag, you have to worry whether it will appeal to a woman, whether it will go out of style … Food never goes out of style. Food appeals to everyone.'

'Can I get some iced water please?' Joyce broke in. 'I must have some iced water. I'm dehydrated.'

Since no one moved, I ran to get her some iced water. When I returned, Grandma was holding Frankie's head in the crook of her arm, as if to strangle him, letting loose a volley of kisses over his trapped face.

''E 'asn't got much 'air but 'e's still 'andsome!' she cried.

Joyce gulped her water and thanked me.

'And what kind of food would you sell?' Dad asked Frankie.

'We're thinking of various menus,' Frankie said.

'How about twenty-eight varieties of omelette?' Jack asked.

'Do me a favour – twenty-eight!' Grandma screamed. 'Cheese, ham, tomato …' she ticked off on her fingers. 'What else can you put in an omelette?'

'Jam, peanut butter, cream cheese,' Frankie listed. 'Peach preserves, apple butter, ten kinds of salami, sausage, ten kinds of cheese, mushrooms, peppers, onions, pâté …'

Grandma screamed with laughter. 'Americans are crazy!' she cried. 'They mix everything together.'

'Baconburgers, cheeseburgers …' Jack told Grandpa. 'No one ever orders a plain hamburger. And they burn the bacon until it's crispy.'

'What do they drink with all this *chuzzerai*?' Grandpa asked.

'Oh … chocolate milk, iced tea, sodas, milk-shakes …' Jack listed. 'Malteds. They love malteds.'

'I could drink a malted right now,' Joyce sighed.

I stared at the brothers as they continued to enthuse about American food. They talked about restaurant *chains*, about a whole new approach to eating out. Their lavish plans and smooth manner made me an instant convert to their message. Would we somehow get swept into this new, glamorous world? My mother's glowing, admiring face made me think we could, but my father's suspicious scowl made it seem less likely.

Grandma hustled Joyce off to view the best room. This was a kind of ritual offered to honoured visitors. We clustered around as she unlocked the door and snapped on all the lights. The glare of hundred-watt bulbs reflected back from all the mirrors, making Joyce wince behind her tinted lenses. Icy air rushed out at us. So silvery and mirrored was the room that it seemed carved from crystal. The sofas and armchairs draped in white sheets added to the surreal effect. I heard Joyce's intake of breath.

'Why, it's … it's …' she groped for the appropriate word. 'It's …'

Looking at the room through her eyes, I mentally completed the phrase for her. It's *hideous*, I surprised myself by thinking. I had always agreed with everyone that the room was gorgeous. Grandma's pride in it was contagious. Now, I suddenly saw that the peach-coloured etched mirrors, their borders showing swim-suited women tossing beach-balls, were in bad taste. The tiny mirrored oblongs covering the entire surface of the cocktail cabinets and sideboards reflected rainbows, as if seen through a prism. The general effect was cheap. It was a shock.

Grandma flicked off the light. 'That's all you're getting,' she announced, as if such a beautiful sight must be strictly rationed. She locked the door.

'Why, thank you so much for showing it to me, Mom,' Joyce managed to say. 'It's very, very ...' she frowned. '*Special*.'

'Eggs and bacon!' Frankie was shouting as we trooped back into the dining room.

'Bacon makes you thirsty,' Grandma countered.

'So they order more orange juice, Ma,' said Frankie, triumphantly. 'Freshly-squeezed orange juice. We know where to get the machines. They're transparent. You see the juice being squeezed out of the oranges.'

'A full British breakfast served twenty-four hours a day,' Uncle Jack cried. 'That's another idea. You think that wouldn't make a fortune?'

I stared at my uncles, trying to see them clearly through the haze of glamour that already seemed to surround them. Together, they somehow formed more than the sum of one and one brother. They created an air of excitement, of unlimited possibilities, of something about to happen.

'Who'd want to eat breakfast twenty-four hours a day?' Grandma wondered, taking an armful of dishes to the door.

'Taxi-drivers, Ma! Nightshift workers, insomniacs,' Frankie said.

'What are you talking about – insomniacs?' Grandma said, always irritable when she didn't know a word.

'People who can't sleep at night,' my mother explained.

'Do me a favour!' Grandma nearly dropped the dishes as she hooted with laughter. 'You're tossing and turning at four in the morning, suddenly you're going to get washed and dressed and go out for *breakfast*?' She left the room.

'I've overeaten.' Joyce suddenly grabbed her stomach, doubling over. 'Could I lie down somewhere? This trip suddenly hit me.'

'Show her my bed,' Grandpa told my mother.

Mum helped Auntie Joyce out of the room just as Grandma returned. 'Is she wearing a corset, Frankie?' Grandma asked, taking a step back to watch the two women progress up the corridor.

Frankie shrugged. 'How would I know?'

Grandma looked affronted. 'A *husband*? A husband doesn't know if his wife wears a corset? It might be too tight.'

'So she'll loosen it,' Frankie said, lighting a cigarette. There was a sudden silence. I watched him take a long, satisfying drag. My brother slipped out of his chair and went to play. Rachel announced that she needed a nap, alongside Barbara on another bed. I knew she would only pretend to sleep.

My mother lit a cigarette and moved to Joyce's seat, her eyes on her brother. 'What could I do in your restaurants, Frankie?' she teased. 'Fry the bacon?'

My father threw her a stern look. 'You don't need to work.'

'If everyone else is working, I'm not just staying at home,' my mother said defiantly. 'What will Joyce do?'

'Joyce?' Frankie laughed. 'Joyce will go shopping.' He stubbed out his cigarette and turned to Grandpa. 'Well? What d'you think, Pa? Sound good? After all, what do you have here? Teashops? Milk bars? Fish and chips?'

'Them filthy-dirty places.' Grandma shuddered, sailing into the room with a tray of steaming cups of tea, the usual end to a meal. ''Eartburn, they give you! *Rats*, they've got!' She passed the cups down the table, followed by a sugar bowl and a plate of biscuits. Grandpa settled into his armchair and dropped off.

Frankie, making a hypnotic clinking noise as he stirred his tea, fixed his gaze on my father. 'You've only just got used to not having rationing here, for Christ's sake,' he said. 'You're grateful if the tea is hot. You don't care what it tastes of. Jack and I kept saying, "Why has nobody else thought of this?" It's too simple, that's why.'

His round brown eyes glowed as he glanced from my

father to my mother and back again. It was as if he had graduated from an American college of fairground barkers. I had seen this scene in several films: the medicine man selling a cure, the confidence trickster setting up the con. Except that this was no confidence trickster, this was my uncle.

'A founding group of four.' Frankie leaned over the steaming tea, his forehead gleaming. 'The two of us! Dad! And you!' He nodded at my father. 'Equal partners. Everyone trusting everyone else.' I watched my father. He was not looking so trusting. His face had taken on that closed-off expression it assumed whenever anyone asked him for something, especially money.

'The more we put into this, the more we make,' Frankie stated.

My mother lit up another Player. The table began to resemble a poker game, with the same blue smoke drifting over the players, the same crafty expressions as they squinted at each other. My father was thinking as fast as he could. I could read his mind. He was wondering how little he could get away with committing and yet remain on good terms with them. Perhaps if he contributed a few thousand pounds these insistent brothers would go away and found their new business and leave him alone. How much backing did they need? How much did they expect? I felt a flash of sympathy for him at having been put on the spot. He had every right to question their overnight schemes, surely? I had no idea what the handbag factory might be worth, or how much it cost to open a restaurant.

'How many restaurants are you boys thinking of opening?' Dad finally croaked out.

'As many premises as we can find,' Frankie shot back. 'Now, before anyone else finds out what we're doing. An opportunity like this, you make hay while the sun shines. I want any copy-cats to wake up one morning and find all the best sites taken.'

Grandma sipped at her scalding tea, beaming. Her sons were making an appeal for funding sound like a precious gift they were offering. They would be doing us a favour to let us join them. That was the attitude. I suddenly realised with a jolt, that if Dad did agree to sell the factory there would be no factory to force me into. He wouldn't expect me to sell twenty-four-hour breakfasts, surely? My career as an artist would be inevitable.

After a few more minutes of scheming, the brothers relaxed back in their chairs, sipping their tea and awaiting some comment from my father. Grandpa was sleeping soundly. Dad shot a look at my mother and cleared his throat.

'I –' he began, but Frankie held up a hand.

'Don't say anything yet, Joe,' he begged. 'Discuss it with Sis. Sleep on it. You may wish to continue with the factory, I don't know what plans you have for it, but …' He made a throwaway gesture.

My father's face was a mixture of many emotions. Indignation was one, for when Frankie said he didn't know what plans there might be, he knew very well there were no plans. 'Plans' was a young man's word and my father had probably never had plans. He had married my mother, accepted half a factory and expected to jog along like that forever. He wasn't ambitious.

'That factory's made us a good living,' he said weakly.

'Get shot of it, Joe,' Frankie said wearily. 'Put the money into something that will make much more.'

'You *hate* the factory!' my mother suddenly burst out. 'You've always said it gives you ulcers.'

My father turned to her. 'Restaurants might give me more,' he said sharply. He faced Frankie again. 'What guarantee would I have that I'd make more money?'

'Joe …' Frankie smiled patiently, shaking his head. 'If business were guaranteed, everyone would be rich! Business *is* risk.'

'So now you're telling me it's risky?' Dad attempted to laugh, but he could never laugh about money, and it stuck in his throat as a dry gurgle. 'I'm supposed to give up my livelihood just like that? A firm I know can pay for my family's schools and clothes and holidays? Give me a good reason to give it up.'

Frankie frowned, biting his lower lip. Then he threw an arm around his brother. 'We're the reason,' he told my father. 'Huh, Ma?' He reached for Grandma's hand and held it aloft, like a boxer winning a fight. 'Two brothers!' he cried. 'Beat that.' Everybody laughed and cheered.

'Also …' Frankie's expression changed to a reproving one. 'You gotta have a *little* faith in us, Joe.'

I stared at my father. How could he possibly not have faith? But as I watched his face, I could see only doubt on it. I turned to my mother. Her face shone with belief. God, this was like a new religion. Either you believed or you became an outsider. And if Dad couldn't believe, how would we stay part of this exciting, American-style, happy family? Oh, sell the factory, Dad, I silently urged. Do something exciting for once in your life!

9

'Who Needs the Brothers?'

The silence in our car going home that night was so intense that Rachel had to wind down the back window for some air. My father felt he had been set up. If he refused to go into business with the brothers, there would be a complete family rift. And could my mother live with a husband who defied her family? Or perhaps she would admire him for standing up to them? My mind raced with the possibilities and I tried to imagine my place in all this.

'A couple of *pishers*,' Dad suddenly exploded, making us jump. 'One who didn't even know to get out of bed on a Saturday – your mother had to tell him.'

'Don't call them *pishers*,' my mother said.

'The other disappears for six years to America and comes back penniless with a *schkop*,' Dad continued, warming to his theme.

'What's a *schkop*?' Lawrence piped up.

'Shhhh, a fat cow,' my mother said. 'What makes you think Frankie is penniless?' she asked my father. 'The house they're renting looks pretty expensive.'

'He didn't even ask the rent,' my father said. 'Your father's paying.'

My mother gazed thoughtfully out of the window. 'It could have been so wonderful,' she said, 'working together like that.'

'Yes? How much of a say you think I'd get?' Dad asked. 'It would be three against one every time. The brothers and your father against me. Because *I'm* not so sure the English will like that type of food. What they love in one country they don't always like in another. In France they eat snails and frogs' legs – does that mean I open a snail and frog restaurant here?'

'Snails, ugh!' Lawrence cried. 'Frogs! Yuck.' He pretended to be sick, very noisily.

'Shut up,' my father yelled. 'There's herring-stalls on every bridge in Amsterdam,' he went on. 'Would herrings make a fortune here?'

'They weren't talking about herrings, Joe,' my mother said quietly.

We passed the drab streets of Kensal Rise and I glanced out at my first primary school, red-bricked and grimy and deserted on a cold Saturday night. I struggled to understand my father's reactions. How could he doubt that the brothers were going to make fortunes – for themselves and for us?

'If their first place does well,' he finally said, 'I'll be the first to invest in their next ones.'

'They won't need you then,' Mum said. 'Everyone will want to invest.'

'And your father didn't seem so keen,' Dad tried. 'A father doesn't fall asleep if he's really excited about his sons' plans.'

'He'd been up since half past five this morning,' Mum cried. 'Anyway, what makes you think he's so in love with that old factory? He'll be only too pleased to get rid of it. And you should be too.'

'Ha!'

There was another silence. We were past Kensal Rise, speeding up Chamberlayne Road towards our house.

Suddenly, my mother burst out, 'So what *are* you planning to do? Dad will want to sell up now, whatever you think. Will you buy out his half? Crank away for another twenty years in that factory? Is *that* such a good investment?'

My father didn't answer. Please don't say my name, I prayed. Please don't say you're counting on your son to breathe fresh life into the handbag business.

'No-o-o …' Dad said. Goose pimples erupted over my body. The back of my neck prickled. 'We'll sell the factory,' he said. My life was changing before my eyes. There would be no factory to force me into. It would no longer exist. 'Who needs the brothers?' my father asked.

'What do you mean?' Mum asked.

'They may be right about people always needing to eat, but who says they'll want breakfasts or omelettes?' Dad asked. 'I think they'll want decent meals.'

The next long silence was my mother's, as she grappled with what he was saying. It lasted until we pulled into the drive of our house.

'You think we could go into catering ourselves?' Mum asked. 'Without any experience?'

'Have *they* got experience?' Dad pulled on the hand-brake very decisively, much more decisively than he actually felt, I could tell. Rachel and I exchanged glances.

We all went into the house and my parents quickly shut themselves into the small sitting room where I usually played the piano. Rachel and I hovered outside the door as Lawrence ran upstairs, oblivious to the drama.

Saturday nights were usually spent watching *Café Continental*, a television show with singers and acrobats. There was no question of that tonight. Rachel bent down, pressing one ear to the door of the closed room.

'They're talking too quietly,' she said, straightening up. Then she tried again. 'I think he wants to open his own restaurant,' she told me. 'Can you imagine? As if *he* knows anything about food. He only eats ulcer food.' She bent down again to listen. I pulled her away, into the kitchen. 'I don't care,' she decided, putting on the kettle. 'All I know is, Uncle Frankie will make a fortune.'

'What if he doesn't make a fortune?' I demanded. 'What if Dad knows better?'

Rachel gave me a withering look. 'If you needed someone to run your business, who would you choose?' she asked. 'Someone young and vital like Uncle Frankie, or someone old and miserly like Dad? I know what Dad will do. He'll buy some cheap, stupid fish and chip shop in some slum, and Frankie, Jack and Grandpa will open huge *chains* of American restaurants. Barbara will invite all her friends to eat free hamburgers and ice-creams and she'll be the most popular kid in her school.' She poured her tea and left, looking back at me. 'I'll never take any of my friends to *his* lousy place. I'd be ashamed to have them *see* it.' She stalked off to her room from where the strains of Johnnie Ray soon issued.

I hung around a little longer, in case any coherent words emerged from the closed room. The quiet discussion was ominous – it meant that Mum agreed with Dad. If not, they would be shouting at each other. What if Dad now insisted I help him in his slummy fish and chip shop? I would reek of fish and the only thing there would be to sketch would be people guzzling from greasy newspapers. I slunk upstairs, depressed.

Lawrence left early the next morning for his Hebrew classes and I exulted in the luxury of not having to attend. I read the Sunday papers and waited for my parents to call down their orders for breakfast, which Rachel and I took in turns to prepare each week. They slept late and did not talk much during the day. The telephone rang only once and I listened from the upstairs landing as Mum spoke to her brother.

'No, not yet,' I heard her say. 'We're still talking about it. Did you sleep well? Beds comfortable? Good. Are you warm enough? Good. Well, okay, yes, maybe tomorrow.' Her tone sounded as if she were trying to sound normal. I tried to ignore the strange atmosphere in the house and practised the piano.

On Monday morning, I awoke to find that my father had left the house early. We would have to take the bus to school. This showed that something very grave had happened or been decided upon. After breakfast, I found my mother in the bathroom, sitting on the edge of the bath, her face in her hands. I rushed to her, taking her shoulders.

'What's wrong?'

She looked up, her face wet with tears. 'Oh, darling …' she dabbed her cheeks hastily, 'I don't like you to see your mother crying. It's just that I haven't slept properly for two nights. Ever since Saturday I've been tossing and turning, wondering if we're doing the right thing.'

'You're not joining the uncles?' I guessed.

She took hold of my hands, pulling herself to her feet. 'Give your poor old mother some of your strength, darling,' she begged, hugging me. I hugged her back as hard as I could, feeling protective but also helpless. She finally broke away to grope in her housecoat pockets for cigarettes.

'I had to let your father make the decision,' she told me as she lit up. 'If I influence him one way or the other, I'd get all the blame if it went wrong.' She exhaled smoke, flicking ash from her skirt. 'If we went with them, we'd probably make a lot of money and we would continue to be part of the family, with Friday night dinners, going out with Uncle Frankie and Auntie Joyce, my mother happy that we were all working together.'

She took another puff and I watched the blue Player's smoke curl around the mosaic bathroom. It was a pretty bathroom with a low, turquoise-coloured bath, matching tiled floor and walls. A kind of blue womb.

'Grandma isn't going to like this,' Mum continued. 'She won't understand why we're not leaping at the opportunity. I understand your father's decision, because if we go in with them, we'll never know what we're capable of achieving. And this is such a wonderful chance for me.'

'Why for *you*?' I asked.

'Oh, darling,' she laughed, shaking her head at me as if I could not see the obvious. 'If your father opens his own restaurant, he's going to need me. We'd be partners. I'd get a chance to go into business.'

'But we need you *here*,' I cried. 'I like having you home when I get back from school.'

'I know.' My mother sat down on the edge of the bath again, pulling me down beside her. 'Let me explain something to you,' she began. Her eyes were alive and glittering as she searched my face for some understanding. 'I'm your mother, right?' She placed her arm around me and gave me a little shake. 'I know that's *all* I am to you. But in *my* mind, *I'm* somebody too. And you know that little thing inside you that's crying out to be an artist? Well, I have a little thing inside *me* crying out to be a working woman. I need to fulfil myself, too, and it won't be by cleaning this house over and over again.'

'You said you *liked* cleaning,' I said, not wanting to accept this version of my mother's life.

'That was my way of trying to make it seem fun,' she said. 'But put yourself in my shoes, darling. Imagine waking up each morning knowing all you had to do was clean this house. And feeling you could do so much more if only someone would give you the chance.'

'And now Dad's going to give you the chance?' I said.

'He's not giving it to me.' My mother exhaled a puff of angry smoke. 'I'm *taking* it.' I must have looked sulky, because she kissed me and went on, 'I've put in my time, darling. Wasn't I always home when you came back from school, making your tea? Didn't I keep this house nice and clean for you all? You children have always come first and always will, but Lawrence will be thirteen soon. I have to think about my own life. When the brothers returned and started talking about –'

'When the brothers returned, everything changed. Everything's different!' I cried. I tried to stand up but she grabbed my arm and held on to me. 'Everything's *ruined*.'

'No! It's not ruined,' she cried. I succeeded in pulling away and getting to my feet. Mum stood up too, facing me. 'This is my chance and you can't be so selfish that you don't want me to take it. I couldn't possibly have raised children that selfish.' Her face looked so anguished that I felt a rush of guilt.

'Oh Mum, I'm so sorry.' I hugged her. 'I didn't realise. Of course if you want to work you should.'

She hugged me back. 'I knew you'd understand, darling,' she said, her voice muffled in my shoulder. 'Of all my children, I knew you'd understand.'

I didn't fully understand, but now I felt obliged to. I tried to picture her slaving away in some kitchen or playing at being a waitress. She stubbed out her cigarette and leaned over the bath to place the plug and run the hot water. She poured the bright green pine essence she used into the water and I inhaled the smell.

'I'm going to take a quick bath and go to see my parents,' she said. 'Your father was there this morning. He'll call me from the factory to let me know how they took it. I'd prefer to remain friends, but you know what Grandma's like. She's very touchy when it comes to her sons.' She got to her feet and opened the door. 'Take your brother to school. You know, I'm rather proud of your father. We won't become as rich as my brothers, but at least we'll be our own bosses. And it'll be better for his ulcer, I'm sure.' She took hold of my arms, staring excitedly into my eyes. 'In time, maybe I'll open my own place, and you know what I want, darling?' I shook my head. 'A sandwich bar,' she sighed. 'Oh, how I'd love that! Somewhere near lots of offices so all the business people could get a quick lunch. No heavy cooking; we'd close at three. I've already thought up some wonderful new fillings. What do you think of mashed banana and chocolate flakes on Hovis bread?'

I swallowed, feeling sick, but she looked so pleased and expectant. 'I ... I ...' I stammered. 'I didn't realise you were so creative,' I said.

'Yes!' She hugged me again. 'I've been lying awake at nights thinking up a whole menu of sandwiches. People must be tired of plain old cheese and tomato – they're ready for something different.'

The bathroom started to steam up from the hot water. I had almost closed the door behind me when I thought of something and popped my head back. 'Does this mean I'll be allowed to go to art school?' I asked.

My mother stepped forward and took my face between her hands. 'Don't look so worried,' she laughed. 'I won't allow any of my children to work in jobs they don't like. I'll make sure you're all fulfilled. From now on we're going to get up in the mornings looking forward to our work.'

I took my brother to school on the bus, staring out at the front gardens we passed, with crazy paving and Monkey Puzzle trees just like ours. Were we really about to enter a new era?

10

The Rift

The first Friday night dinner Grandma held for her reunited family demonstrated that we had not reunited, after all. Despite the blazing chandeliers, the best tableware, the chicken that had stewed for two days, we did not feel the usual welcome. There was an underlying atmosphere, a false note beneath the usual hugs and kisses and cries, which it took me a while to identify. It was pity. As if we poor children were the victims of my parents' bad judgement in not joining the new enterprise.

Bowls of steaming soup were carefully carried down the long corridor to the dining room. Everyone made a great fuss of the *gedempt* chicken once again and asked for second helpings. Grandma even treated herself to a generous Scotch to celebrate her family eating together on a Friday evening for the first time in memory.

'We've been looking at some lovely restaurants,' my mother chattered brightly. She had been eagerly awaiting this chance to talk shop with her brothers. 'We saw a very nice Italian place on Old Compton Street in Soho –'

'Soho's full of streetwalkers!' Grandma cried.

'We turned that one down,' Frankie said shortly. 'Too small.' He said nothing about his own search for sites.

'Anyone tryin' to find a decent place in London now will only get my sons' leavin's,' Grandma declared with a cackle.

My parents exchanged looks. My mother's mouth tightened, a new resolve making her chin jut rebelliously. She had not expected war to be declared so soon.

'I think you boys are looking for different things to

what we're looking for,' my father began to explain to Frankie. 'As I see it, you're looking at very busy streets with lots of passer-by trade.'

Frankie shrugged, reaching for another piece of chicken. 'We're looking at everything,' he claimed.

'Whereas we're looking to take over a small, established place,' my father continued.

I wondered why he was being so cringing, why he didn't simply tell them to go to hell? I felt terrible for my parents. Why should my uncles care about their one restaurant if they were planning entire chains? As they continued to chew their chicken in silence, their arrogance made me burn with indignation. I wished I had the authority to express what I felt to them.

'Now they've got more backin' than they need, it's just a question of their findin' the locations,' Grandma told my parents. She had suddenly become her sons' surprisingly articulate spokeswoman.

'What do you think of Soho, Frankie?' Mum asked him. 'It's said to be the up-and-coming area.'

'My sons are only lookin' in the most expensive streets,' Grandma answered quickly. 'Oxford Street, Bond Street – places *most* people,' she gave Mum a pointed look, 'can't *afford* to buy in.'

I glanced at Grandpa. He looked uncomfortable, as if under strict orders not to discuss business. Negotiations to sell the factory were under way and he managed to steer the conversation to that. Later, my mother made a few more unsuccessful attempts to talk shop, but her brothers' curt replies made it clear that they felt their grandiose plans placed them in an altogether different sphere to my parents' amateur fumblings. Dad retreated into an offended silence, and Mum chattered manically with Joyce about shopping. Soon the telephone in the passage began to ring and Frankie and Jack ran in and out, taking or making calls, too important now ever to be part of a family meal again.

We left early, another first. On the drive home, my parents analysed every dig Grandma had made. They sounded so hurt, especially my mother, that I became doubly hurt on their behalf.

'I never thought they could be like this,' my mother said wonderingly. 'I thought they'd give us a little advice.'

'Advice,' my father growled. 'They'll make us lick their windows before they give us advice.' This was a new expression to me and I mimed licking the car windows to my sister. We doubled up in silent laughter. 'Maybe we should feel complimented that they think of us as competition?' Dad added.

'I think we simply don't matter to them, now,' Mum said. 'We didn't join them so they're going to ignore us. Well, I'm never going to Mother's for dinner again.'

Rachel and I exchanged looks.

'Don't be ridiculous, of course you have to go,' Dad said.

'What for?' Mum asked. 'To be insulted and made to feel small?'

'Can I still visit Auntie Joyce?' I asked. Her rented house had become my favourite stopping-off place on the way home from school. It was like visiting Manhattan.

'You can visit her, but don't mention Soho to her,' Mum said.

'You already mentioned Soho!' my father pointed out.

'Yes, but if they hear *how* interested we are, they might suddenly decide that they like Soho and then we've had it.'

'What are streetwalkers, Mum?' Lawrence suddenly asked.

'People who like walking in the street,' Mum said quickly.

'What's wrong with that?'

'Oh, you know how funny your grandmother can be,' Mum laughed.

'Are we really going to buy Uncle Frankie's leavings?' Lawrence asked.

'Now will you be quiet!' My father made us jump. 'No one's buying anyone's leavings. It's none of your business, anyway. Your job is to do well at school.'

We did go to the next Friday dinner after all. Dad

insisted, but he said that if anyone was rude to us, we'd never go again. This time, the uncles didn't even bother to show up. Joyce and her daughter came and Uncle Frankie made a brief appearance at the end of the evening when he came to collect them. He was offhand and abrupt, and when I saw the hurt look on my mother's face I vowed never to forgive him. He had been her idol and now he had disappointed and humiliated her. She hadn't expected much from Jack – he just aped his big brother.

Over the next few weeks my parents shopped around for a restaurant as if they were buying a pair of shoes. They had expected some guidance from the uncles, but were now thrown very much on their own instincts. A serious crime had been committed, in Grandma's view. Someone had doubted her sons' money-making abilities. The penalty was banishment from the magic kingdom of the brothers, a kingdom that Grandma's friends, family and cronies were all clamouring to be admitted to. It was beyond Grandma's reasoning to see that my parents were choosing a quieter, more modest life where they could be their own bosses. Their decision to go their own way could only be interpreted as a head-to-head battle with the brothers. From now on, we were the enemy!

Neither my mother nor my father had ever shown any great interest in food. When Mum roasted a chicken, she would only allow me to chop one small clove of garlic to sprinkle over the bird. The heady aroma of the stuff was like a drug and I begged to be allowed to chop more. But one clove was the limit, otherwise we might 'smell of garlic'. Nothing we ate was highly spiced. Our larder held no curry, no chilli, no paprika, chutneys or pickles. Our sole experience of pasta (a word we didn't know) was the occasional tin of Heinz spaghetti, which we ate on toast. So the news that my parents' choice had narrowed down to an Italian restaurant was cheering. Better than a fish and chip shop.

'But who'll cook Italian food?' I asked my mother.

'Mario,' my mother beamed. 'He comes with the restaurant. He's a wonderful chef from Italy.'

'What if he leaves?'

'We'll find another chef, darling. Don't be such a worrier.'

Yes, I had inherited my father's tendency to worry about possible calamities way in advance. I hoped that didn't mean I was going to have ulcers too.

'What's the restaurant called?' I asked.

'Ciao,' my mother told me. 'That's Italian for goodbye.'

My sleepless, worried nights began from this moment. It couldn't be as easy as my parents thought to suddenly become restaurateurs if you had never done it before. How could they know all it involved? How did they even know what an Italian dish should taste like? If it had been a restaurant serving ulcer food to worried businessmen they would at least bring some experience to the game. But this!

My mother would try to soothe me, sitting on my bed late at night when I couldn't get to sleep. 'We'll learn as we go,' she assured me one evening. 'The owner – Mr Ross – is staying with us for a fortnight to show us the ropes. He'll practically train us – that's part of the deal. I shall greet customers and take their orders. Oh darling, it's so exciting! I've done it a few times and I love it. I'll have to buy some new work clothes; I've only got housework rags or good clothes, nothing in between.'

I couldn't continue to list my worries when my mother's eyes glowed so, her excited smile lighting up her face each time she spoke of Ciao.

'So it's practically certain?' I asked her.

'Well, we're still thinking it over,' Mum said, bending to kiss my forehead and getting to her feet. 'We'll see what Grandpa gets offered for the factory. He's going to split whatever he gets with your father. Then we'll know if we can afford to buy Ciao.'

*

I knew I should make the most of my limited welcome at Joyce's rented Brondesbury house, which happened to be on my route home from school. I loved dropping in there of an afternoon and being transported to New York.

'What I miss most about the States is the plentifulness,' Joyce declared.

She did her best to recreate it in north-west London. Sweets had only recently gone off ration, so the bowls of candy and jelly-beans were quite enough to convince me that her living room was the most beautiful room in London. The house was glamorous and exciting, from the coloured-in outlines of Joyce's orange lips and her Technicolor hair, to the jelly-bean flavours of watermelon, papaya and blueberry. Bowls of popcorn, dishes of salted nuts and bright pink sacks of bubble-gum were dotted around the room, all to be washed down by unlimited cream soda. Treats that were special events in our household were everyday here. Music played constantly, songs from Broadway shows that had not even reached London. Every room in the house had its own television set, left on day and night, if only to flicker out the test-card. It gave the impression that a lot was going on, even if the only thing actually happening was Joyce reclining on a giant sofa, bolstered by piles of glossy American magazines like *Look*, *Saturday Evening Post* and *McCalls*.

'It's open house here,' Joyce would laugh. It was certainly the most careless, generous, expectant atmosphere I had ever encountered. My father got furious if someone left a landing light on. Here, Joyce was angry if I turned a light off. 'Oh, put it back on, p-l-e-a-s-e,' she would drawl. 'It's so *dark* in England.'

She popped corn on the huge American stove that they had installed. There were no fixed mealtimes; whenever Joyce took it into her head to roast two dozen 'franks' on a sheet of foil in the oven was a mealtime. Drenched in American mustard, they were served on warmed rolls. She bought up the entire range of American foods stocked by Fortnum and Mason in their Exotic Foods section. Joyce made me realise that if you were rich, you could be careless. Rich people could leave the lights on all night, the television on all day. Rich people could spill things and nobody minded – it didn't matter. They could buy another table cloth or television set. Uncle Frankie might not be rich yet, but he acted as if he were. Or perhaps Aunt Joyce had unlimited money of her own: she acted as if she did.

Sometimes Grandma would be there, ensconced in the most comfortable armchair, sitting as though on a throne, upright and critical. Her black cloche would be firmly pressed down over her ginger hair and she would gaze imperiously around her, finding things to disapprove of. Joyce refused to hang net curtains over the wall of windows overlooking the garden, and Grandma considered this unsafe because anyone could peer in from the back garden; she had once glimpsed the gardener. All the treats Joyce tried to press on her mother-in-law were haughtily turned down. 'No thanks. Makes you fat.' Only towards the end of her visit might Grandma accept a cup of tea, saying, 'because I'm a bit dry …', a dig at the strong central heating, which was always turned up full blast. Joyce and Frankie had all the latest gadgets, even a fridge that dispensed crushed ice.

'All that fancy machinery and she can't even make a decent cup of tea,' was Grandma's comment.

Sometimes Uncle Frankie could be glimpsed rushing through, picking up messages or making phone calls before running back to his huge Chrysler to visit more properties.

'I guess we'll buy this house,' Joyce shrugged. 'There's no time to look at others. I mean, it's fine,' and she would shrug again. I wished I could adopt her shruggy attitude to life. I was careful now not to make any references to Soho. Instead, we discussed Deborah Kerr, who I felt ought to be a Sunday school teacher, but whom Joyce admired, saying that she was 'such a lady'.

On my last visit, I was watching Joyce pop some corn when the doorbell rang urgently, five times. Joyce nodded for me to open the front door, her hands full of buttered popcorn. I found two little ragamuffins and one older boy, leaning against the doorway with the cocky attitude that kids have when they know they shouldn't really be there.

'Let 'em in!' Joyce nodded. 'They're Barbara's friends.'

Perhaps Americans gave the word 'friend' a looser definition, but I doubted this lot were friends. They ran in, greeted Joyce nervously, grabbed handfuls of candy and rushed into the garden. We watched as they climbed the swings Frankie had set up for Barbara and the little girl greeted them.

'She's made so many friends here,' Joyce sighed. 'She loves it.'

'And you?' I asked.

The clever eyes gleamed from behind their tinted lenses. 'I'm adapting,' Joyce said. 'I miss my parents, of course, but your grandmother's very sweet and Frankie's so sure we'll make a lot of money here. He says there's no competition.'

She widened her eyes as if to say that people here were too stupid even to try to compete with Frankie. But I was starting to question her grasp on reality. Perhaps *she* was the stupid one. Did she really believe these kids were Barbara's new friends? Didn't she realise they only came for the candy? And who in their right mind could describe Grandma as sweet? Hadn't she realised that when Grandma ate nothing in your home, it was an insult?

'Your hair looks nice,' I said, guilty at thinking these thoughts.

'Mmm, needs colouring,' she said, running her fingers through the bright yellow waves. 'It's so hard to reach the West End from here. I must learn to drive.' My mother had told me that Joyce went to the most expensive hair salon in Mayfair, one that Princess Margaret used. 'No one else can get that gold colour,' she sighed.

I stared at the framed wedding photograph of Joyce and Frankie. Joyce looked pretty – and half the size she was now. Frankie was thinner too, with more hair. They looked so happy in the photograph. Were they happy now? I had heard my mother complain that Joyce was 'cold'. Once she used the word 'frigid' and I immediately looked it up in Freud. 'Unresponsive,' Freud explained. 'Unable to be sexually aroused.' Could a woman be aroused? Didn't they just let men do it because they wanted children? I couldn't quite picture Joyce in a sexual situation. When we met, she gave a kiss into the air, touching neither face nor cheek. I had thought this might be to protect her carefully drawn-on lips, but perhaps it was the kiss of a frigid woman?

'Gotta have more iced water,' Joyce gasped, scrambling to her feet, possibly to get away from my intense scrutiny. While she was out of the room, I glanced at the wedding photograph again. Frankie's smirk was cocky. Although he always greeted me with a friendly slap on the shoulder, in repose his face was pugnacious. When he arrived home at night, the crowd of kids and hangers-on were unceremoniously shooed out.

I kissed Joyce goodbye and left, uncomfortably full of popcorn, candy and Joyce's life. I had heard my parents whispering that Joyce might be pregnant, which would explain her heaviness and laziness. Uncle Frankie hadn't called Mum and she was sad about that. Were we really going to be enemies with that side of the family? I compared Joyce's marriage to my parents'. Did my mother think it would be easy being Dad's business partner? An uneasy feeling in my stomach told me that there were lots of worries ahead and I couldn't help feeling anxious.

11

Clearing Out the Factory

'Grandpa asked if you'd help him clear out his office tomorrow,' my mother said one Friday evening, a few weeks into the family rift.

'But it's Saturday,' I wailed. 'I always go to the pictures.'

'It would be nice of you, darling,' she said. 'He especially asked for you. He might be a bit sad, closing the factory.'

I grudgingly agreed.

I rang my grandparents' bell at noon the next day and was ushered in by Mary, chattering away. Grandma was preening herself in front of her dressing-table mirror, dressed and made up and with an air of great importance. I kissed her freshly powdered, chalk-white face.

'Don't let yer grandfather get near them big machines,' she warned, kissing me back. 'If they get turned on by accident 'e'll lose an arm.' I watched her ram her black satin cloche down over her orange hair, Mary clucking and fussing around her. 'And don't let 'im take the lift by 'isself. The gates jam – 'e could catch a 'and in them.'

Mary helped her on with an immense black Persian lamb coat. Voluminous and stiff, it stood straight out from her body. She carefully buttoned each button.

'Where are you going?' I asked.

Grandma's green eyes peered out mischievously from beneath the hat. 'We're invited for lunch at the Cumberland,' she announced. 'Mary and I are walkin' up there.' She used the Cumberland Hotel as an extension of her sitting room, visiting it for tea or to watch the people from a central table in the lounge.

'And what's the occasion?' I enquired.

From behind Grandma, Mary rolled her eyes at me, jerking back her head and muttering. 'Oh, I s'pose they want to get on my good side, eh Mary?' She gave a roguish laugh.

Mary nodded and pulled on her own shabby black coat, ushering Grandma to the front door.

'Be careful with your Grandpa, darlin',' Grandma threw over her shoulder. 'Watch 'im! Don't let 'im lift anything 'eavy.'

Half an hour later, Grandpa and I were driving through the busy Saturday streets in Grandpa's silver Triumph.

'Why was Grandma all dressed up?' I asked him.

Grandpa chuckled. 'She's promised her friends she'll see them all right.'

'See them all right?'

'You know, with the boys.' When I still looked blank, he gave an impatient nod. 'All Grandma's friends sell something, or their children do. Sheets or towels or kitchen supplies. They want to sell to the boys and they need your grandmother to put in a good word. So they're taking her out for lunch, buttering her up.'

I liked the idea of Grandma all warm and buttered, served up like a slice of toast. From now on, she would reign as the Queen of the Cumberland Lounge.

'Why didn't you come for dinner last night?' Grandpa suddenly swerved off the main road. He had begun driving before licences were invented and it showed.

'I ... I didn't know we were invited.'

'Suddenly you need an invitation?' he grunted.

He must know what was going on, I thought. He wanted to show me that *he* still wanted us there at Friday night dinners. We pulled up before the ancient grey building in Kentish Town's most undistinguished road. Grandpa's factory occupied the fourth floor, the other floors being divided between various manufacturers that produced a weird assortment of products, from mouse-traps to plastic combs. The building was so quiet it seemed as if it had ceased operations overnight. What would become of all the workers, the old 'leather men', whose hands were stained tan, or Miss Cropley, the gangling grey-haired spinster secretary who resembled Olive Oyl and who answered the telephone in her shaky voice, 'Gulliver one-four-one-oh?'

Grandpa unlocked the front door and we took the rickety lift up. He had to push hard against the factory door because it was blocked with post. No one had been there for a few days. The factory, usually abuzz with machinery and people, was silent. The aroma of glue and leather hit me the moment he opened the door wide. As a young boy, I had been lifted onto a stool by a grizzled leather-worker, an apron placed over my clean clothes, and set to work folding rectangles of card for reinforcing handbag corners. My tools had been a large square slab of a marble-like substance, and a bone spatula for ironing out the fold. I had taken pride in folding several hundred.

Before we reached the cavernous factory floor we went through a dark warren where panelling with frosted glass inserts sectioned off some offices. Grandpa's had a curious, three-dimensional portrait of himself, done in coloured and folded papers, that made him look Churchillian.

'Your Uncle Frankie wants this,' he told me, removing it from the wall and wrapping it in newspaper. 'Probably wants to make a dartboard out of it.' We stared at the pale rectangle on the wall, which years of Grandpa's cigars had not stained khaki.

'How old were you when you started this place?' I asked, as we walked out on to the factory floor.

The space echoed with our footsteps. I glanced up at the paper-chains from the last Christmas party still dangling from clumsy fluorescent lamps. The windows were streaked with soot.

Grandpa hummed the Figaro aria under his breath as he touched a mound of blue leather off-cuts on a work-bench top.

'Oh … thirty-eight, thirty-nine, maybe,' he began, then broke off to say, 'Remind me to keep a special box just for 1956. I know those tax people – that's the year they'll drive me crazy about. I need all the receipts. I'll beat them at their own game.' He found a large paper sack and swept the bits of leather off the work-bench into it.

'Did you come here straight from the Paris Opera?' I asked.

'Here.' He pushed the bag at me and motioned to his office. 'Go through all the cancelled cheques on my desk and find the ones made out to the Inland Revenue. That's proof we paid our tax. Destroy the others.'

'Well?' I asked.

He frowned at me. 'Oh, yes, the Paris Opera. That was long before this. I was in my twenties then. I came to England when I was twenty-four.'

'So it took fourteen years until you were able to start up a factory of your own?' I asked.

'Why do you need to know all this?' Grandpa muttered.

I had never been able to get exact dates, figures and facts. Not about the factory, not about anything in the family's history. How had he found the backing? Had Grandma's family been rich? Something told me it wasn't the right moment to ask these questions, although in our family it was never the right moment.

In Grandpa's untidy office, the contents of files and boxes had been tipped out and rummaged through in a hurry. There were files marked 'Employees', 'Insurance', 'Orders' and 'Receipts'. Many simply sported large dates: 1938, 1939, 1940. In the pile of cheques I found two made out to the Inland Revenue and handed them to Grandpa when he entered the office.

'Good,' he said, pocketing them. 'Destroy the others.'

'Why did you choose handbags?' I asked.

Grandpa sighed, sitting down in a swivel chair. I had thought he would enjoy telling me the history of his factory, but he seemed irritated.

'When we lived in Whitechapel,' he began, 'we ran this handbag stall in Petticoat Lane. I worked for a friend of the family. Another, older fellow taught me how to repair the straps when women brought them back and complained they had broken. It was because they carried too much weight in their bags, but we repaired them for free, to keep our customers. These were my tools …' He indicated the marble-like slab he kept on an iron stand in his office. 'I kept this to remind myself how I began,' he said softly. 'I can still repair a handle.'

'So you repaired handbags on a stall. Outdoors?' I prodded.

He nodded. 'Rain or shine. Some winters we nearly froze. Then we had to start charging for repairs – they were bringing back bags that were years old! Women started to ask for special designs, so we made bags to order. Found a few workers, rented a garage, and we grew. Your father joined me and we started working with better quality leather. Selfridges took us on.' He shrugged, spreading his hands. 'And today we close.'

'Oh, Grandpa.' I went over to hug him.

'Progress, darling,' he shrugged again, tracing a line on the waxy slab with a rusty old cutting-wheel. 'Those sons of mine are as bright as buttons. If they say people will always eat, I'm not going to argue.'

'How old are you, Grandpa?' I asked.

'Sixty,' he said.

Yes, I thought. That was old.

We took some boxes downstairs to the rubbish bins at the back of the building. When we got back inside the factory, I asked, 'What about the clock?' There was a beautiful old wall-clock high on the wall, so large that the second hand seemed to take ages to sweep its face. It had been placed so that each worker could see the time and not down tools a second before five o'clock.

'The new owners can have it,' said Grandpa, glancing up at it. 'It's too big for anyone's home.'

We began to work again, sorting through stacks of papers, throwing out as much as we could. Dusty boxes, files, papers and correspondence dating from the first years of the factory, were tipped into rubbish bags and taken downstairs. We made the trip several times.

'I can't finish this today,' Grandpa said at half past four. He stood over his desk looking at his collection of tools. 'I'll have to come back again next week.' He touched the slab and picked up a long, pincer-like tool. 'What the hell am I going to do with all this stuff?'

'Keep it,' I urged.

He hesitated, then suddenly winked at me and swept the lot into his overcoat pocket. At that moment, there was a long ring from the bell downstairs.

'That'll be your Aunt Hilda,' Grandpa said. 'Go down and let her in, will you? She wants a last look at the factory.'

Hilda was standing tiptoe on the top step, peering in through a murky pane. When I opened the door, her face relaxed into a smile.

'You must both be dying for a cup of tea,' she cried.

She bustled in, a large plastic bag on her arm, with the top of a thermos flask peeping out. She greeted Grandpa with consoling clucks and for a moment he clutched her to him, holding on to her. They both regained their poise and she unpacked the little picnic that she had brought. The bag contained piping-hot tea in a flask, sandwiches and cakes. Milk and sugar were in miniature jam-jars, obviously saved for just such an occasion.

'All right, are you, Mr G?' She handed him a steaming plastic cup.

'A little tired,' he admitted. He sipped his tea as Hilda gazed around his office.

'Such memories,' she sighed, shaking her head. 'I began my career in catering here.'

'Is this where you met?' I asked them.

Grandpa suddenly backed up his chair with a harsh scrape against the floor. He stood up.

'Children are getting too nosy these days,' he growled at me, passing his cup to Hilda for more tea. He took the tea and strode out of the office.

Hilda lit a cigarette and smiled at me through the smoke. 'Don't mind him, dear,' she said, seeing my hurt face. 'It's not you he's angry with. This is very hard for him. No man likes to give up his power, not even to his sons.' She took a long puff, then stood up and walked to the door of the office where she gazed out on to the factory. 'New

York's given your uncle a new lease of life,' she told me. Her bright little eyes sparkled as she glanced back at me. 'He's finally realised that he doesn't need his mother's permission to get on with his life.'

'But –' I walked over to stand near her.

'She'll throw a thousand fits, your Grandma,' she said. 'And don't I know who'll bear the brunt.' She jerked her head towards Grandpa. She stubbed out her cigarette. 'Look at him,' she said, 'this is wrenching his guts out.'

I stared at her. 'Wrenching' and 'guts' were not words I associated with Grandpa. 'He says it's progress,' I said.

She turned and fixed me with a fierce bright stare. 'Yes, because he doesn't want to upset anyone!'

Later, we cleared away the tea things, rinsing the cups in the large, square cracked sink in the lavatory. We stacked the bags by the front door and I watched Hilda powder her nose with quick dabs, compact open on the palm of her hand. She applied fresh lipstick in one practised slick and patted her bun. Then she stalked off across the factory floor in her echoing high heels.

'Come along, Mr G,' I heard her soothing voice say, 'you'll finish up here another day.'

12

'Don't Leave Me!'

Grandpa offered Hilda a lift home. She sat down with a sigh of fatigue on the front seat, glad not to have to repeat the two-bus journey home. When they reached her narrow street, she leaned across to give him a long hug. I thought it was the fond hug of two old friends. How could I see Hilda the way Grandpa saw her, or Grandpa the way Hilda saw him? She must love him as much as I did, I decided, to the extent of doing anything for him.

Grandpa drove very slowly into his own street. I glanced at him: he seemed very tired. Uneasily, I watched him as he made several fumbling attempts to get the car into generous spaces, eventually giving up. He seemed to have lost the ability to park his car. Finally he managed to park a little crookedly in a large space, slumping back in his seat as he turned off the engine.

'Grandpa?' I got out and came around to his side 'Are you all right?'

He did not answer, but handed me the keys to the flat. 'Go on up. I'll be up in a few minutes,' he said hoarsely. The orange light from a nearby lamppost made his face look sickly. I opened his door.

'Let me help you,' I offered.

He didn't move. His eyes were closed. 'Go on up, darling,' he said faintly. 'I just need five minutes.'

I began to walk to the entrance to the flats, then changed my mind and returned. 'I think I should come with you,' I said.

He opened one eye. 'Five minutes,' he begged.

I hesitated, not sure that leaving him was such a good

idea. If I let him doze for five minutes might he not fall into a deep sleep, from which it would be even harder to rouse him?

'Come on, Gramps!' I pulled at his arm. 'It'll be much harder later.'

He tried tilting his head back to see the windows of his flat. 'Is she watching?' he asked.

I craned back to see: some windows were lit, but there was no silhouette of Grandma peering out. 'The coast is clear,' I said. Grandpa made an effort to haul himself up, his face creased with the strain.

'We don't want to worry your grandmother,' he gasped, leaning on me.

Our progress up the carpeted stairs was agonisingly slow. My arm ached from the weight Grandpa put on it, but I was determined to get him to his flat.

'Only one more flight,' I urged him on.

'I'll be fine once I sit down,' he said. 'Pour me a brandy and I'll be as right as rain.'

It took a long time to reach the front door. After guiding Grandpa to where he could lean against the cream embossed wall, I fumbled with his keys. I had never used them before and it took several tries to unlock the top lock. As I pushed the key into the second lock, the door was suddenly pulled open. Grandma greeted us, still in her Persian lamb coat, her face suffused with whisky and triumph.

''Allo, darlin',' she cried. 'I thought I 'eard you.' The pleased expression on her face lasted a split second longer as her gaze swept past me to my grandfather, and he chose that moment to slump to the floor. Grandma's eyes widened. 'Oh my God. Max! Max?' She flew to him and took his head in her hands. The light streaming out of the flat flood-lit his sickly face. 'Speak to me, Max!' she screamed. 'Talk to me!'

'I'll get some brandy,' I said, running inside.

Grandma's screams, a series of short animal cries, followed me through the flat as I hunted for a glass and poured a shot of brandy. I ran back outside. Grandma was rocking Grandpa in her arms like a baby, whimpering over him. The primitive moaning froze my blood. I reached over to pour some brandy into Grandpa's mouth, but it dribbled down his chin.

''E's dead,' Grandma announced.

For a moment she seemed beaten, and utter misery flooded her face. Then she gathered herself together. Gazing upward, she shook her fist at the unknown entity who had dared to do this to her. I had never seen anyone shake their fist at God before. Then she grabbed the lapels of Grandpa's overcoat and began to shake him in earnest.

'Max! MAX!' she yelled into his face. 'Don't leave me, Max. DON'T LEAVE ME!' She glanced helplessly at me, her eyes bulging with fear. 'Help me,' she begged. 'Get him back!' She placed her hands inside his coat, rubbing at his heart.

I shook his shoulders, shouting, 'Grandpa! Grandpa!'

'Don't leave me, Max. DON'T LEAVE ME!' Grandma cried again. No one appeared on the staircase to help us. Perhaps they had heard Grandma's screams too often to find them unusual. 'Max! Don't leave me. Oh, *please* don't leave me.'

The piteous cries echoed in my head for weeks. Later, Grandpa swore that he had died, but that on hearing Grandma's screams, he had not dared continue his journey. He came back to assure her that he was going to be just fine, if only she could be a little quieter. Together, Grandma and I managed to get him on to his bed where he promptly fell asleep.

Then Grandma did something she very rarely did. She telephoned for the doctor.

*

'Your husband has suffered a mild heart attack, Mrs G,' Dr Kossoff said in his beautifully modulated British accent. Boris Kossoff was the best-spoken, most assimilated Jew we knew. To me, he seemed to be a cross between James

Mason and Basil Rathbone. Like them, he appeared to be playing the role of a distinguished English gentleman. I thought him a complete phoney.

'A 'eart attack? A 'eart attack? Oh, my *God*!' Grandma screamed. 'Oh, my God, what are we going to *do*?'

Dr Kossoff looked around for something to eat. We were in the kitchen following his examination of Grandpa. He was adept at grabbing a perfect peach or plum from a fruit bowl, but that day it held only apples or oranges, none of them suitable.

'Oh my God, a 'eart attack,' Grandma moaned again.

'A *mild* heart attack,' Dr Kossoff said reprovingly. He had a unique way of dealing with Grandma: he treated her as if she were a completely normal human being. 'He needs a week or two of complete rest. Has he been under any particular strain lately?'

'Strain? I should say not!' Grandma cried indignantly. 'With sons like '*e*'s got? 'E's going to be on easy street, doctor.'

'Delighted to hear it, but –' the doctor glanced hungrily around the kitchen.

'He has been a little upset about selling his factory,' I said. 'We've been there all afternoon, clearing up. There's a lot to do there, and Hilda said she –' I broke off, remembering too late that Hilda's visit had been top secret. Grandma acknowledged my slip with a flash of her green eyes and a 'wait until later' look.

'He's closing his factory?' Dr Kossoff raised his eyebrows. 'That could be stressful for him. Is there any whisky around, Mrs G?'

Grandma frowned. 'Should 'e be drinking?'

'I meant for me,' Dr Kossoff said. He obviously thought that if he couldn't enjoy some fruit, he might as well get a drink.

Grandma nodded. 'I'll join you,' she said, sweeping out of the kitchen and returning with a bottle of Scotch and two tumblers. 'I nearly 'ad a 'eart attack myself seeing my 'usband passed out on the floor like that.' She poured two generous shots and clinked glasses with the doctor. 'My 'usband's 'ealth!' she proposed solemnly, swallowing the drink in one professional gulp.

The doctor sipped at his. 'So he's somewhat sad at closing down?' he said to me.

I nodded. 'He loved the factory.'

'*Loved?*' Grandma's head jerked up. 'What are you talking about? 'Ow could 'e love *that* filthy place? Rats, it 'ad. The workers drove 'im mad. 'E'll be glad to see the back of it. 'E'll be sittin' in a lovely new restaurant, takin' the money, watchin' the world go by. My sons are openin' American restaurants, doctor,' she added proudly. 'Tell all your patients to eat there – do 'em the world of good.'

'Er, yes. I certainly shall.' The doctor glanced at me, found a prescription form and began to scribble his indecipherable handwriting. I eyed the smart Parker pen. 'Perhaps your grandson could fetch this, Mrs G?' he suggested. 'It's only a mild sedative. To make sure he sleeps. Give him one every evening and keep him in bed. I'll be by tomorrow to see him. When he's feeling better we'll arrange some tests.'

''E's not going to need any kind of … operation, then?' Grandma asked fearfully.

She liked Dr Kossoff because of his perfect bedside manner and his ability to arrange things.

'We'll have to see; hopefully not,' he said. 'I think Boots will still be open,' he said, shifting a stiff white cuff to glance at an expensive watch, handing me the form.

I went off to Boots, happy to do something constructive to help Grandpa. The doctor had left by the time I returned. Grandma was rinsing the whisky glasses and seemed undecided about what kind of mood she should be in. Her make-up had suffered cruelly from the screaming and weeping and she hadn't bothered to repair it. Traces of tear-streaked olive skin showed through the white, caked powder.

'I'm not wakin' 'im up for *these*,' she declared contemptuously, staring at the pills I handed her. ''E'll sleep right through till tomorrow without no pills.' She led the way to the bedroom and we looked in on Grandpa. 'Look at 'im, sleepin' so peacefully,' she snorted. 'As if 'e 'ad no idea of the terrible shock 'e's given me.' We walked back to the kitchen. ''E 'asn't 'ad no 'eart attack, neither,' she said, glancing at me. 'That doctor doesn't know what 'e's talkin' about. Likes to put the fear of God in you, 'e does! Makes more money that way.' She banged the kettle onto the stove. 'One of 'is funny turns, that's all it was. 'E's 'ad 'em before – remember that time at the pictures? Sleeps 'em off. I'll make some tea. You'll stay until my sons get 'ere, I don't want to be alone.'

She busied herself with teacups and teaspoons, disappearing to change into satin slip, apron and slippers. She poured the tea a little distractedly. Delayed shock reaction, I diagnosed.

'Did you 'ear 'ow I screamed?' she asked suddenly.

'How could I have missed it?' I said.

'I thought 'e was a goner, I really did,' she said, her eyes brimming with tears. 'I could see myself layin' roses on 'is grave. Yellow ones, 'is favourites.'

She began to sob, one hand up to her eyes, the other supporting her weight on the sink's edge. I jumped up and put my arms around her as she shook and just for a moment she allowed herself to be comforted. Then she brusquely pushed me away and blew her nose noisily. She had to save some emotion and tears for her sons. She sat down with her tea, pushing mine over to me.

'Of course, I don't think it was the factory that upset 'im.' She stirred her tea thoughtfully. 'I think it must 'ave been that 'Ilda.'

We hadn't discussed my little slip. I watched her carefully. This was called 'baiting': saying something so outrageous that I would jump at the bait and reveal some more secrets.

'Can't think what *she* was doin' up there,' she said, sulkily, when I didn't answer. 'A woman of that age, carryin' on like that.'

'She only brought us some tea,' I said.

'Oh, yes?' Grandma nodded. 'She's very good at tea, *she* is. Used to be a tea-lady.'

'Yes. She told me. A long time ago.'

Grandma sniffed. 'It's a wonder she remembered the address.' She saw I was not about to say more about Hilda, so she changed the subject. 'I thought *I* was gonna 'ave a 'eart attack when I saw 'im,' she said. 'I thought 'e was dead.'

She continued to recount new versions of the afternoon's events. She would try out several until she found the most effective, then she would make that the official one.

'And I'd just 'ad such a lovely lunch with my friends,' she said. 'We was quite merry. I was expectin' you both, I was still in my coat, wasn't I? I 'eard the key goin' into the lock, but you couldn't work it, could you? I wondered why 'e 'ad *you* open the door, and I got worried. I opened the door and saw 'im lyin' there. Oooh, God, did I start screamin'! Did you 'ear me screamin'?'

I nodded, suddenly weary of the story. I would have heard it many more times if the uncles hadn't arrived, allowing my escape. I could hear Grandma's screams as I walked down the street. She would enact the scene for her sons until she had squeezed every ounce of drama – and then humour – out of it. They would laugh, hug her, applaud her performance, top up her whisky. Grandma had triumphed again! The night Grandpa almost died. The night her screams brought him back. It would pass into family myth.

13

Keeping Mario Happy

My sister and I thought we had better taste than our parents. We were more modern, more in touch, knew quality when we saw it. Possibly most children feel this way, but especially children of Jewish immigrants, raised in better conditions than their parents. This snootiness reared its head the moment my parents announced their interest in an Italian restaurant. We had not been shown the place; my parents were not going to be influenced by what we thought. We wanted any restaurant to be fun and attractive, whereas they only cared about the potential profits.

'It'll be a dump,' Rachel predicted, and I agreed. I imagined a 'caff' with stained menus, grimy table cloths and listless waitresses barking 'Off!' to most dishes.

The owner, Mr Ross, sent an invitation via my parents to lunch one Saturday. Perhaps he thought that if we liked it, we would push our parents into making an offer? We set off in Dad's car on our best behaviour, prepared to be disappointed. Old Compton Street was the first surprise: it was Soho's liveliest, most atmospheric street and at its best on a Saturday, as shoppers hunted down Italian foods. The aromas of olives, cheeses and freshly-ground coffee drifted out of the narrow doorways of the delicatessens. Continental couples – French or Italian – bought *Paris Match* or *Oggi* and with bulging baskets stopped at favourite coffee-bars for cappuccinos. It made a wholesome background for the plastic-macked prostitutes plying their trade up and down the street in clicking stilettos.

'This is it!' my mother cried. She was as proud of Ciao as if it were already hers.

We followed my parents into the café. With a shock of pleasure, I took in its unexpected chic. A bar along the far wall held eight tall stools. A dozen tables, each with four wooden, curved chairs, huddled close together under a hanging ceiling in an inverted V-shape, decorated in warm earthy colours – an Aztec design. The round grey-blue Formica table-tops had silkscreened photographs of sunflowers on them. The floor was black-tiled and a large window overlooked the activities of Old Compton Street. We could not ignore what the main activity was.

'Tarts,' Rachel hissed, as two painted girls strode by.

'Don't call them that,' my mother hushed her. 'They're lovely girls. They pop in for coffee all the time.'

'Probably need it,' Rachel nudged me. 'After *that!*' We broke into suppressed giggles.

Ciao was full. Some customers were eating toasted sandwiches, others were sipping from what looked like goldfish bowls of coffee and foam. Others were deftly twisting strands of pasta around their forks, like unravelled knitting. Shopping bags spilling with groceries were tucked beneath chairs and a cosy buzz of different languages and blue Gauloise smoke swirled around the room.

'Well, hello.' A tall, slim Englishman in tweeds stepped forward. 'This must be Rachel and you are either Lawrence or Howard.'

'Howard,' I said shyly. 'This is Lawrence.'

'Splendid.'

Mr Ross shook our hands and, whisking away a 'Reserved' sign from a window table, drew up a fifth chair. He seemed terribly English to be running an Italian restaurant. A little awed, we followed his bony finger as it guided us through the menu, hand-painted on a gondola shape.

'These are the pastas,' he began.

'You know, like spaghetti on toast,' my mother added.

'There's also tagliatelli, ravioli, cannelloni, lasagne …' Mr Ross went on, 'and you can have them with Bolognese or Neapolitana sauce.'

'One's with meat, the other's with tomatoes,' Mum put in.

We all chose spaghetti, but my father chose *Osso Buco*, the most expensive dish on the menu. We stared around us, unable to believe that this smart place could ever be ours. Mario the chef came out of the kitchen to take our orders personally. He was an intense Italian with a twirly moustache and the traditional tall chef's hat. His face was steamed bright scarlet and his eyes twinkled as he ran back into the kitchen with our orders.

'He'll whip you up something special,' Mr Ross promised. 'He wants to impress you. Can't wait to get rid of me, y'see. He thinks if you really enjoy this meal you'll buy Ciao.'

My parents laughed politely.

'No. The thing to remember about Mario, Mr Conway,' Mr Ross hunched forward, 'is to keep him happy.' He fixed my father with an intent stare. 'If Mario's happy, this place runs like clockwork. I really can't emphasise that enough.'

'He seems like a nice man,' my mother offered.

'We-ell …' Mr Ross frowned. 'Mario's an artist. He has an artist's temperament. I've worked with him for ten years – it hasn't always been easy. If something upsets him, he'll down tools and walk out. Oh yes!' he nodded at my parents' alarmed expressions. 'Even midway through the lunch-hour. I've had to scamper after him to the nearest pub and beg him to return. You've never seen a prima donna in a chef's hat knocking back double brandies in a fit of pique, have you, Mr Conway?'

'No,' my father said.

'It's not a pretty sight,' Mr Ross said. 'Yours truly on my knees, crying "Mario! Come back! We love you! You're the best chef in Soho!" ' He burst into laughter at his imitation of himself. 'But keep him happy and he's the easiest person in the world to work with.'

The table fell silent as a dark-haired waitress set our places. Finally, my father asked, 'And how *do* we keep Mario happy?'

'Ooof.' Mr Ross gasped as if he had been winded.

'That's the sixty-four thousand dollar question. Well. To begin with there's no cutting corners with Mario. Don't try smuggling a cheap pasta past him or substituting corn oil for olive. He won't let you.' He laughed at the absurdity of the chef giving the orders. 'Mario *will not* let you,' he repeated. 'But he's a bloody good chef,' he added. 'Bloody good!'

My father, who never swore, winced at each 'bloody'. I suddenly realised that Mr Ross reminded me of the comedian Terry-Thomas.

Our mountains of spaghetti, topped by avalanches of Bolognese sauce, were served with great pride by Mario himself. He held aloft a dish of grated Parmesan cheese, raising his eyebrows. We each nodded, cueing a snowstorm of scattered cheese. A giant peppermill then ground a hailstorm of black pepper. Finally he returned with what looked like a bone left over from the Stone Age: my father's *Osso Buco*. He wished us '*Buono appetito*!' and vanished.

I twisted the first strand of pasta around my fork, the way I could see the other customers doing. The taste was completely fresh: mushrooms, herbs, tomatoes, wine. The tang of Parmesan cheese blended it all together. I had read that Picasso concentrated very hard when signing a picture. Not wanting even his signature to be banal, he attacked the page as if signing for the first time. Mario did that with spaghetti. No matter how many thousands of times he had prepared the humble dish, he always put a little bit of his soul into it. We savoured each strand, watched approvingly by Mr Ross as he sipped his tiny *espresso*.

'And you're not eating, Mr Ross?' my mother enquired.

He laughed. 'You'll feel the same if you last ten years,' he said. 'One day you see one too many a pasta dish and suddenly you can't face the stuff. I'm so sorry.'

My father made a strangled noise of enjoyment. He was eating his dish as if he had never eaten before.

'When I bought this place,' Mr Ross suddenly told us, 'I vowed to work non-stop, very hard, for ten years, save up the profits and escape to the Virgin Isles. That's exactly what I'm doing, and I shall be the laziest man you've ever seen.'

We stared at him in admiration. Both the ten years' hard work and the idea of being lazy on a tropical island seemed unbelievably glamorous and clever. He indicated our plates, which were practically licked clean.

'Now this is how Mario likes dishes to return to the kitchen,' he said. 'Always give new staff strict instructions to scrape plates clean. If he sees anything left, Mario takes it personally. He's been known to walk out if that happens.'

'It sounds as if he's always walking out, this Mario,' my father said, giving up on getting any more marrow out of his bone.

'No, no,' Mr Ross assured him. 'You'll find a way to rub along, I'm sure.'

We ordered cappuccinos instead of desserts: my first sip of the strong coffee intoxicated me with its rum-scented taste. The only mishap came when Lawrence, balancing a teaspoon of grated cheese over my sister's cappuccino, hiccuped and spilt the cheese into her coffee. My mother restrained my father from cuffing him around the head, and Mr Ross fetched a fresh cup. When my parents began to question Mr Ross in earnest, we took a walk around Soho, Rachel and I watching the prostitutes' activities over Lawrence's head. We saw them meet clients and about-turn to march back to their doorways, nestled between shops and cafés and marked by doorbells reading MODEL or DISCIPLINE.

'I wonder how long they take?' Rachel whispered.

We were driven home in a happy daze.

'I think we're going to buy it,' my mother announced in the car.

That evening, the familiar groans came from Dad's bedroom. The rich Italian food had met the ulcer head-on. Matters were not helped by the strain of having to make a new financial commitment. We tiptoed around, frightened of disturbing him, scared he would change his mind about Ciao.

A small flat above the restaurant came with Ciao. It was used as a storeroom for huge canisters of oil, cartons of pasta, stacks of tomato purée. There was some furniture, including a bed, which Mr Ross said he sometimes slept on or allowed staff between shifts to take naps on.

The important element in the deal – Mario – was said to like my parents and had agreed to stay on if they bought the place. The next few weeks were tense as we waited to hear Mr Ross's reaction to my father's tentative offer. I think Mr Ross had taken a liking to my parents and wanted Ciao to fall into their hands. He probably felt they would not tamper with his winning formula, cherishing the idea of diners feasting on dishes which he and Mario had created: restaurant immortality.

In October we learned that Ciao was ours. We whooped and danced around the house. Now we would be able to eat as much spaghetti and sip as many cappuccinos as we liked, and all for free! I would get to know the waitresses: Leonie, a lovely Greek girl with white skin, cascades of dark hair, red lips and flashing eyes, and Marie, an older, blowsier blonde who reminded me of Mae West. I was sure both had interesting life-stories to recount and both would prove useful models.

'And Mum already knows some of the prostitutes,' Rachel swooned. 'They tell her about their work and everything. If we wait at the window long enough, we'll see how long they take.'

I didn't understand why the timing was so important to her, but we hugged each other in delight. All that research to do. We were going to eat better and know more about the world's most ancient trade than any other children in Willesden – perhaps the world.

*

I took to Soho and felt at home there. It was bigger than I had realised, stretching from Oxford Street to Shaftesbury Avenue, taking in Chinatown and parts of Charing Cross Road. My favourite street was Wardour Street, because the film companies filled their windows with exciting posters advertising forthcoming films, but Charing Cross Road exerted a raffish pull with its second-hand bookstores and cinemas showing 'Continental' films, a code-word for sex. Several black-windowed stores were simply called Marital Aids, yet another code-word for sex, I now knew.

Just before Foyles, which claimed to be the biggest bookstore in the world and yet was strangely unexciting compared to Better Books across the street, a grey block of granite announced St Martin's School of Art. I liked to hover outside this school, inhaling its aura.

One Saturday, as I stood in its doorway, peering up at the frieze of easels, palettes and draped ladies, the door opened and a cleaner with a cigarette dangling from his mouth emerged to fetch two dustbins from the kerb. He trudged back, dragging the bins, and I followed him inside. The entrance hall held a notice-board from which posters, announcements and flyers fluttered in the draught. A blackboard announced: 'New Term 23 January 1957' and a table held piles of prospectuses. I took one. The most interesting course – if you were as unsure of your career as an artist as I was – was Foundation, a 'general course lasting one academic year' open to 'students over sixteen who submit a current work portfolio'. Did a half-filled Woolworth's sketchbook count as a current work portfolio? I read the course description hungrily: Modelling, Outdoor Drawing, Abstract Design, Drawing from the Clothed and Unclothed (my pulse quickened) Figure! Optional Evening Classes in Silkscreening, Graphics, Photography. And only a minute's walk from Ciao. If I begged for this test year, promising to abide by the school's assessment of my worth, could my father refuse?

14

Marital Aids

Grandpa's attack, mild or not, brought home to me how much I would miss him if anything happened to him. I saw, too, the depth of the family's terror when it came to illness. The scary phrase 'heart attack' had quickly been replaced by 'funny turn'.

'Why is everything so hushed up?' I asked my mother on the bus to visit Grandpa, a week after the attack. 'He should know what's wrong with him so he can be more careful.'

'You can't change them, that's how they think,' Mum said. 'Grandma's made Dr Kossoff promise not to tell him. She thinks if Grandpa knew, he'd have another heart attack. I mean funny turn.'

Grandpa was sitting up, dressed, on his bed. He was getting regular cups of tea, and meals were brought in on trays by Grandma or Mary. He looked pink and comfortable.

'I'm being treated like a king,' he greeted us. 'The only thing I miss is a good cigar. My wife doesn't let me smoke in the bedroom.' We laughed and tried to cheer him up. 'I was a goner, y'know,' he said, fixing first me, then my mother with serious eyes. 'If your mother hadn't made such a row, I'd have continued on my way. It was nice and peaceful … no different to having a nice long *schluff*.'

'Don't say that, Pa,' my mother begged. She had to leave the room for a moment to dab her eyes. Grandpa used the opportunity to ask me to pop in to make sure Hilda knew he was recovering. I promised I would.

'How are the boys doing?' my mother asked when she came back.

'Racing the clock,' Grandpa said. 'They want the place open by December to catch the Christmas shoppers.' He tapped the side of his head as if only his brilliant sons could think of that.

The new café was to be called the Egg & I and was due to open on Oxford Street. It was the first of a planned large chain. They had found firms and banks to back them and would franchise branches.

'The boys go up to Manchester next week,' Grandpa winked. 'I'll be fit as a fiddle by then. I'll smuggle you in to take a look.'

Although she was slightly offended by the idea of being smuggled in, my mother was too curious to resist. The following week, we went to the boarded-up site near Oxford Circus and asked for Grandpa. True to his word, he seemed quite fit as he ushered us into the large space, bustling with carpenters and electricians. Even half-finished, it was outstandingly ugly.

'It doesn't look American at all,' I whispered, disappointed. 'Just cheap and plastic. Ciao is a hundred times nicer.'

My mother looked at me pityingly. 'But this will make the money,' she said.

The decor relied entirely upon the fried egg motif, with table-tops in white and lurid yellow and the cashier's booth, in which Grandpa was to sit, a brown and white egg pyramid.

'Two hundred and fifty seats!' Mum marvelled, making a rapid count. Her eyes gleamed as she pressed my arm. 'One day we'll have a place as big as this.'

The uncles became known as the 'Egg Boys' and were featured in the business-pages, grinning from behind plates of fried eggs. Grandma cut out the photographs, crying: 'They're the 'andsomest sons in the world!' Weren't the photographs proof of this? They were tipped as the next big success story, with banks, investors and even egg-farms queuing to invest in the chain. The queue now included my father who had decided to swallow his pride and ask to be a sleeping partner.

*

We were called in to our parents' bedroom at the end of the week. It was nine o'clock in the evening and Dad had not been down to dinner. He was sitting up in bed, sipping from a square bottle of paraffin. This could only mean aggravation and ulcer pain.

'The uncles are not letting me invest,' he announced.

'I knew it,' Rachel cried. 'You should never have asked them, Dad. You shouldn't have lowered yourself.' Because she was a girl, she sometimes got away with saying stuff that Lawrence and I would be slapped for.

Dad put down the paraffin and stared at her. 'You like to eat, don't you?' he questioned. 'You like going on holidays and buying new clothes?' He waited for her to nod. 'Well, where d'you think the money's going to come from?' he cried.

Mum looked sad. 'Their places will be fantastically successful,' she said. 'We could have all been working together.'

'I'd rather work as a dustman!' Rachel cried.

'And I'd rather work in Ciao,' I said, rashly.

'Fine.' My father seized the moment. 'You'll be cashier on Saturdays. That way I can help your mother serve.'

Rachel and I exchanged looks.

'Grandma could have smoothed things out,' my mother said. 'It's as if she wants the feud to go on.'

'It doesn't matter, Mum.' Rachel hugged her. 'Soho's a million times better than Oxford Circus. We'll be selling quality food. They'll just get people dripping egg yolk over their clothes.'

'You'll stop visiting Auntie Joyce, darling?' My mother looked at me. 'I'm sorry, but I'll never forgive them for this.'

I called Joyce from a telephone box near school. 'It's okay. I understand, Howard,' she said in her breathy drawl. 'I'm sure it'll all blow over and we'll get back to being friends. You're not missing much – your grandmother's dinners get heavier each week.' She was nearly six months pregnant and sounded exhausted.

'Will I see you when you've had the baby?' I asked. 'Even if it has to be in secret?'

'Oh please,' she groaned. 'Aren't there enough secrets in this family already? I've never seen such a family for secrets.'

I laughed. 'I've met Christine,' I told her.

'You have? Well, you're one up on me. What's she like?'

'She's very nice. Very pretty. They're very much in love.'

'Yeah?' Joyce asked dully. 'Wonder if they'll marry? Maybe it would take a little attention away from me, huh? I know Mrs G thinks I'm overweight. I can't help it, I always eat for two when I'm carrying. I get these cravings for ice-cream and before I know it, I've got through an entire tub. And Frankie's almost never here. He's always viewing properties. He's never here to help me *fight* these cravings. I get lonely and I *eat!*'

She began to cry softly over the phone. 'I try so *hard*! But, let me ask you something, Howard, how strong d'you have to *be*? Huh?'

I wasn't sure how to answer, so I stayed silent, listening to her weeping. 'Please don't cry, Joyce,' I stammered. 'You'll feel a lot better when you've had the baby.'

My idiotic attempt at consolation had the effect of turning her sobs into giggles.

'I don't know if I'll feel a whole lot better, exactly,' she hiccuped, 'but I'll sure feel a lot lighter!'

The Egg & I opened by serving a thousand free fried eggs to its first customers. There were riots in Oxford Street. It was as if no one had ever eaten a fried egg before. Our part of the family decided not to attend the gala opening. I'm not even sure we were invited. We heard that a famous pop star had cut the yellow ribbon and that a dozen girls dressed as eggs had jigged in the windows. 'The Egg Brothers Strike YOLK GOLD!' the newspapers said. Grandma was photographed between her two sons, beaming and hugging them. From then on, there would be no stopping them. Backed by Grandma's bragging and seemingly unlimited funds, they became London's flashiest millionaires. It all seemed to happen overnight.

*

Mr Ross stayed on at Ciao for the first two weeks, teaching my parents everything he knew. My mother hung on his every word. She asked us to be understanding and help her through this difficult period. We returned home from school every day to an empty house and meals that had been left to be heated up. I would serve early dinner to my brother, and we would do our homework and watch television until bedtime. We were in bed asleep when my parents' car drew up in the drive. Mum advertised for a full-time maid in the local newspapers and announced that she was going to take driving lessons. In Willesden, in 1956, this was roughly on a par with George Sand smoking cigars in public in nineteenth-century Paris.

'You'll never pass the test,' my father jeered.

'Then I'll just keep taking it until I do,' Mum answered cheerily.

I heard her insist on a weekly salary so that she could have her own money. This, too, was a departure from the weekly housekeeping my father had previously, grudgingly, handed her each week. Mum was struggling to be free and Dad was doing everything he could to resist it.

One evening, I heard her say: 'Well? Am I an equal partner or not? Plenty of restaurants in Old Compton Street would employ me. I've been talking to some of them.'

He gave in.

That first trial fortnight of work was a mere taster of what was to come. Catering hours were gruelling and long. Soho mornings were fairly lazy and late, but once the lunch rush hour got under way, Ciao was busy until mid-afternoon. Coffee and cake customers filled the gap between lunch and pre-theatre dinners, which often started at six. Dinners could go on until one or two in the morning. By the time they gave lifts home to chef or waitresses, my parents did not get to bed much before three. My mother thrived on this and visibly bloomed. My father seemed to be in shock from being on his feet so many hours and sleeping less.

*

It was January 1957. Wearing my heavy coat, scarf and gloves, I perched in the cherry tree, staring at the back of our house. The branches of my favourite tree were quite bare, almost black. It was difficult to believe that in a few months fresh green leaves would sprout. Since my uncles' return five months before, everything had changed. Grandma no longer welcomed us to her home. Mum was an independent businesswoman, learning to drive.

My brother would soon be starting barmitzvah preparations with Rabbi Kaplan, but no one even noticed. I was worried about Grandpa and had visions of him clutching at his heart while locked in that pyramid of plastic eggs. I wouldn't be there to help him and Grandma wouldn't be there to scream at him to come back.

I did my cashier work at Ciao on that first Saturday after my parents took over, self-conscious and terrified of giving the wrong change. I watched my mother greeting customers and showing them to tables. She was pretty good at it, balancing a pile of menus on one arm, smiling and shoe-horning two couples into the same table, whether they wished to share or not. She got a little too good at greeting, sometimes pulling in people from the street when they were only peering in, undecided.

'Some of them need a little push,' she laughed when I scolded her.

As Rachel had predicted, Mum became friends with the prostitutes, 'the girls' as she called them. She even off-loaded some of her old clothes onto them. I sometimes ran after a familiar jacket or coat on the street, pulling at what I thought was Mum's arm, only to have a garishly painted tart turn around eagerly to me. 'They like my taste,' my mother boasted, but it showed me that her taste was a little flashy.

Once I watched the blonde waitress Marie giggling with Leonie, the Greek waitress, over something one of 'the girls' had told them over coffee. 'What were you laughing about?' I asked Marie when the girl left. Marie started giggling again.

'She was telling us about a man who tried to put it in her ear,' she said. I went bright red and thought about it for weeks afterwards.

Mum bought herself some new work clothes, which were closer-fitting than usual. 'So I can squeeze between tables,' she told me. She lost weight. She took to being in the public eye. Her smile was dazzling and when businessmen lunched in pairs, she would take their arms as she led them to a table, and they liked it. As far as I could see, this was pretty innocent and just Mum being charming. But I had been having disturbing thoughts about whether my parents still had sex and asked Rachel what she thought.

'Don't you hear them on Sunday mornings?' she asked. She seemed to enjoy shocking me.

I frowned. 'I thought it was just Dad tickling Mum and her giggling?'

'She giggles,' Rachel agreed. 'But not just from that.'

Once or twice I found Dad in bed when I got home from school in the late afternoons. He would be lying on his side, groaning, as he sipped from the ever-present bottle of paraffin. Sometimes I felt a little sorry for him. His life had changed so dramatically and he did not really seem suited to his new role.

'Your mother wants us to serve dinners until two at weekends,' he told me.

'So?'

'Our licence only lets us serve until one. I worry that there'll be a police swoop on us. They come in all the time – they expect free meals.'

'If you give them a few free dinners, they'll let you stay open, won't they?' I said.

He groaned, sipping from his bottle. 'The uncles haven't personally served a single fried egg,' he said. ' They get managers to stay up until all hours. They delegate.'

'Mum says nobody takes as much money as when you and she work there,' I pointed out.

'That's true.'

He lay back in the bed. I watched him go to sleep. He had always reacted badly to strain and worry: weren't we proof of that? All three of us would feel that jump of fear whenever we spilt something for the rest of our lives. Strain made his ulcer act up, which irritated him, which caused him to lash out at the nearest person. With all that was going on – his pain, the changes, the lack of sleep – I suppose it was inevitable that he would find a new victim.

*

On the final night of Mr Ross's supervision – a Friday – he offered to keep an eye on Ciao while my parents came home for dinner with us. He must have known it would be our last family meal for a while. It was wonderful having Mum bustling in and out of the kitchen again, making Welsh Rabbits. She loved to improvise picnics, more snacks than meals. It was half past seven and my father's face was taut as he leafed through the paper. He was hungry or tired, or possibly in pain from his ulcer. Perhaps he was missing the handbag factory where work had always ended at five o'clock.

'Oh, I'm going to enjoy this,' Mum announced, popping the last Rabbit onto a large platter and bringing it to the table. She gave us one each and took one for herself, drenching it in Lea and Perrins.

'Put lots of sauce on,' she instructed my father, 'you'll like it.' She bit into the melted cheese and sighed. 'Mmmm, I was so looking forward to this. I'm getting a little tired of Italian food. It's good, but not every day.' We listened as she chatted away, telling us that a famous singer we often watched on television had been in for lunch that day. 'And she was *tiny!*' Mum marvelled. 'You expect them to be so tall.'

We were so impressed at hearing about their first celebrity customer that no one noticed the dark mood enveloping my father, pulling tighter and tighter until it had to break. My mother got to her feet to fetch more toast from the kitchen.

'Prostitute!' Dad cried suddenly.

He threw his dirty plate at her. It crashed against the wall, just missing my mother's face. The chink of broken china clattering to the floor froze us as we all stared at him. So he's finally lost his mind, I thought. My mother's face flushed as she bent to gather the broken pieces of plate.

'Prostitute!' my father cried again, standing and pointing at her, his voice high and strained.

We watched my mother straighten up, her face blank. It was like a scene from a dream, not real life at all. She took a deep breath, as if coming to a decision to reply.

'What are you talking about?' she asked, rather haughtily.

My father jabbed his fork at her. 'You think no one noticed,' he cried in his cracked voice. The Polish accent had returned. 'You were up in the flat with Mr Ross. A woman alone with a man. You stopped up there for a quarter of an hour. You think no one noticed?'

His eyes were starting out of his head, the vein in his temple enlarged and throbbing. Perhaps he would have a heart attack and drop dead, I thought. He looked as if he were about to pounce on her. I tensed, wondering if I would be strong enough to pull him off.

My mother laughed, like a Hollywood actress acting out a role.

'Are you seriously suggesting that Mr Ross and I …?' She laughed again, the laughter sounding a little forced, even to me. I ignored that. She was nervous because Dad was so crazy. She was probably quite frightened. She wouldn't want to show him she was frightened, the way we had been taught to act calmly around big dogs. They smell your fear, my mother had told us.

'Well? What are people going to think?' Dad cried. 'A woman and a man alone.'

'People?' Mum echoed. 'What people? Mr Ross was only showing me the soup.'

'What soup? What are you talking about?' my father asked, frowning. 'Mario makes his own soup.'

'No, they use Heinz tomato soup on Mario's day off,

didn't you know?' my mother asked, almost cheekily. 'Mr Ross was showing me where they keep the stock, that's all. I'll show it to you tomorrow.' She seemed quite fearless, her eyebrows slightly raised at Dad as if he were a bit stupid. 'If I were going with a strange man, at least give me the credit to choose one of the young waiters,' she joked.

Again, it sounded as if she was trying to keep the mood light. But something was missing from this scene: shouldn't she have been more angry?

'You broke a perfectly good plate,' she admonished him, shaking her head.

We all remained quiet. Mum pushed open the door to the kitchen and we heard her slip the broken china into the rubbish bin. She returned with pan and brush and swept up the little bits. Dad sat down, looking nonplussed. It was so absurd, his calling Mum a prostitute because she had gone to a store room alone with Mr Ross, that I felt almost sorry for him. And I also felt a surge of admiration for my mother: she knew how to defuse situations. My sister and I dared not catch each other's eye – Dad might notice and throw a plate at us. My brother used the moment to pour himself a brimming glass of orange squash.

'Okay,' Mum said, coming back into the room and sitting down again. 'Who wants another one?'

She offered the platter around. There were no takers, so she finished eating what she had started.

'I told the Italian grocery we'd be ordering more pasta next week,' she addressed my father. He didn't answer.

'Which pasta do you sell most of?' Rachel asked. 'Spaghetti?' They were trying to turn the conversation back to food.

'I'd say ravioli,' I said, to keep it going.

'You're both wrong, it's tagliatelli,' my mother laughed.

Dad still said nothing. His eyes were on my mother, slightly angry, slightly puzzled. Rachel and I got the evening back to some semblance of normality but it was hard going. Something within me found her reactions odd. I was thinking furiously fast. Mum was too calm. Shouldn't she have protested much more hotly? She was brushing a very serious accusation under the carpet, which was unlike her. Could she possibly be in the wrong?

Suddenly, Dad scraped back his chair and stood up. We all flinched. He turned and left the room. We heard his heavy steps on the stairs and the slam of their bedroom door.

'Oh. Gone to bed early,' my mother said lightly. 'I expect his ulcer's acting up.' We watched her as she stared dreamily into space for a moment.

'How *could* you?' Rachel burst out. 'How could you let him talk to you like that?'

Mum shrugged, smiling. 'Because it's so ridiculous, darling. I just have to laugh. He's under a strain, he has to shout at someone.'

'But he called you a prostitute, Mum!' Rachel said. She began to cry.

'Oh, don't cry, darling.' Mum moved to put an arm around her. 'Your father's a very jealous man, that's all. I should feel flattered that he thinks every man is after me. But Mr Ross, really! He's so English, such a gentleman, do you think he'd do anything disrespectful to the wife of the man buying his business? No! And anyway, he isn't my type at all.' She laughed with a wild devilry in her eye I had never seen before.

We helped to clear the table, washing and drying dishes, throwing away the pile of Welsh Rabbits that everyone had lost their appetite for. She was our Mum, I thought, as I dried the last plates. She could only be one hundred per cent in the right. Always. Some kind of angel or saint who worked so hard to make our lives comfortable, who told us that we made life worth living for her. She had scrubbed out hotel baths with Vim so that her precious children would not feel the dirt of other people. She had once come to school to see that some bullies who had victimised me were properly punished. She listened to all our problems and tried to solve them. Could this woman possibly flirt with men?

It took me a long time to get to sleep that night. The disturbing images of my mother with the so-polite, gentlemanly Mr Ross kept me awake. Soho had started all this, of course. Wicked, thrilling Soho had forced the unmentionable – the unthinkable – into our lives. The prostitutes, the brazen way they stalked Old Compton Street in their stilettoes, had somehow made the selling of sex seem everyday and normal. As did the mysterious Marital Aids stores. Now perhaps my parents would need their wares? I remembered that new expression I had seen on my mother's face, that rebellious, wild devilry. I made myself imagine her going upstairs with Mr Ross to look at cartons of tomato soup, heard her laughing at his jokes, saw her turn on the staircase to catch him looking at her legs. The knowing look in her eyes, her giggle when Mr Ross reached out to touch her. I felt sick. But it was not beyond the realm of my imagination, after all. Something in me knew my father had not completely invented the story: he was not imaginative enough.

I tried to adapt to this revelation. To see my mother as a woman who craved admiration and my father as a jealous man who had been provoked. 'It Takes Two to Tango' an Alma Cogan song currently told us. 'Two to really find the meaning of romance …' The annoying ditty played in my head as I drifted off to sleep. I felt I should cry for the loss of my mother's image as angel or saint, but I couldn't. There was something almost thrilling about watching my parents' marriage fall apart.

15

The Secret

When the worry build-up got too heavy, I sought out Grandpa. His humour and gentle philosophy, accompanied by a few arias from *I Pagliacci*, usually did the trick. One wintry afternoon, I caught the bus from school to the Edgware Road, hoping I would find him just back from his lunchtime stint at the Egg & I.

He was not alone. Mary opened the front door, muttering under her breath and pulling faces. She wore her black coat as if she were about to leave and raced back to the kitchen. Grandpa was resting on his bed, shoes off, legs crossed, eyes closed. Jack's room was a flurry of activity. I glanced in – Jack was packing. Not an overnight bag but three large suitcases. It looked as if he was moving out. I headed for the kitchen. Grandma was slumped at the table, her eyes red, her mouth turned down in a grimace. She stared into an empty whisky glass. Mary jerked her head towards Grandma and rolled her eyes at me, miming something with her lips. I had stumbled into a battle zone.

'I'll be going now then, Mrs G,' Mary said, very loudly. 'See you tomorrow.' Grandma didn't move or speak. 'Your grandson's here, now. That'll be nice for you,' Mary said, edging towards the door. She fixed me with a desperate gaze, shaking her head.

'Bye, Mary,' I said, watching Grandma.

Mary took off down the corridor; we heard the front door close behind her with a slam of relief. Grandma glanced up. She was wearing her official grieving outfit: a very creased white nightgown.

''E's leavin',' she announced, pouring herself another shot of whisky.

She raised her voice: 'You give them all the advantages, they make a little money, and suddenly they think they can do anything they want!'

'I'm a big boy now, Ma,' Jack's voice came back. 'I don't need your permission anymore.'

'Oh, isn't *that* nice?' she screamed. 'But you needed my permission to run to America, didn't you? You needed my permission all those Saturday nights when you didn't know what to do with yerself and I found you friends to go out with. You needed my permission –'

'Yes, but I've grown up now, Ma. I can think for myself.'

Grandma shot me a red-eyed look. 'Think for 'isself!' she repeated. Lifting her head, she took a deep breath. 'A son with a little respect for his mother doesn't move in with no *shiksa*.'

'Christine's a wonderful girl,' Jack called. 'Pop likes her. Why don't you try to?'

'*Like*?' Grandma frowned. 'A *shiksa*?'

'She's studying with a rabbi. She knows more about our religion than we do.'

'She can study with a 'undred rabbis, they won't change her blood.'

'So what do you want? A blood transfusion? She'll do it.'

'I want *Jewish grandchildren*.' She shook her head to herself. 'Is that too much to ask?'

'They'll be officially Jewish. And you'll love them.'

''Ow could I love grandchildren who aren't even circumcised?' Grandma shuddered, pouring herself another whisky.

'If they're boys, they'll *be* circumcised.' Jack's head suddenly appeared around the kitchen door. 'Howard here can be one of the ten men at the *bris*.'

'Oh, thanks a lot!' I said. About the last thing I felt like witnessing was the circumcision of an innocent baby.

'They won't let you marry in a synagogue,' Grandma said sadly.

'Oh yes they will. The rabbi said so. The Liberal.'

''Er parents can't stand under the *chuppah*.'

Grandma had played her trump card. When it came to fine details of the Jewish religion, she could be surprisingly knowledgeable.

'She only has a father. So you and Pop will stand under it, okay?'

'No, it's not okay.' Grandma glared at her son. 'Do you want to kill your father? He's had *one* funny turn, do you want to give him another?'

'I've never felt so healthy in my life.' A resigned groan came from the bedroom. 'You're the one making all the *geschrie*.'

Grandma stood up wearily and poured some boiling water through a tea-strainer full of tea. She added milk.

''Ere.' She thrust the cup at me. 'Take this into 'im. *I* can't look at 'im. 'E never backs me up.' I took the tea into Grandpa's room as Jack returned to his packing.

'Thank you, darling.' Grandpa took the cup and sat up on the bed, carefully balancing it. He winked. 'How am I supposed to get a nice little nap with all that going on?'

I watched him sip his tea. 'Do you really feel well, Grandpa?' I asked.

'Never felt better. The restaurant is packed all the time. When are you coming in for a meal?'

I avoided his eyes. 'I'm … not that keen on eggs,' I muttered.

'I've made a lot of new pals,' he went on. 'The customers like to tell me their problems. Especially young girls – secretaries and such. They seek my advice.'

'You're a good listener,' I told him. 'They all think you're their grandfather.'

He winked at me again. 'Maybe you'd better go in and help your uncle.'

Uncle Jack didn't seem to need my help. He was on his third suitcase. The first two, closed and locked, stood by the door. He gave me a nod, pressing down a pile of shirts. Suddenly he tossed a dressing gown at me.

'Can you use this?'

I didn't feel I should take anything from him but it was too luxurious to resist. Green, orange and yellow tartan, in a wonderfully soft wool, the label said 'Simpson's'. I had never dreamed of shopping there.

'Thank you,' I said, folding it carefully.

He tossed me a plastic bag to put it in. 'I should have done this years ago,' he muttered, half to himself. 'I must have been out of my mind to put up with all her *mischegas*.'

'*My mischegas*?' Grandma screamed from the kitchen from where, incredibly, she had overheard. 'With all the thousands of beautiful Jewish girls in London, you couldn't find *one* you liked? Your brother found one.'

'Did he?' Jack shouted right in my ear. 'Or did he find an easy way to get an American visa?' This explained a lot. I filed it away to be examined at some future date.

'At least she's Jewish,' Grandma yelled.

'So why haven't you stopped criticising her since she got here?'

'Because she's a lazy fat *schkop* who's good for nothing but shopping and spending money,' Grandma cried. 'I'm 'er mother-in-law! I've a *right* to criticise!'

Jack stopped packing for a moment, straightening up, shaking his head. 'Do you know any other families like this one?' he asked me, conversationally.

'I –' Before I could reply, he crouched down beside me, fixing me with his black, dark-lashed eyes.

'Listen,' he said, urgently, 'do me a favour. Christine's waiting downstairs. I didn't realise this would take so long. We're moving into a flat next door to Hilda's building. Go down and stay with her for a few minutes. Tell her I'll be right down.'

'I … I'm not sure I'll recognise her,' I blurted.

'A pretty blonde in a grey Jaguar,' he said. 'There's only one down there.'

'All right,' I sighed. 'And thanks for the dressing gown.' I kissed Grandma goodbye. Her nightgown made her look like some Moroccan peasant selling her wares at market.

'You don't know all I done for them,' she said dully,

turning her deadened grey stare on me. She looked as if she were about to pass out. ''E didn't even know what night was til 'e was fourteen …' she muttered. ' "Mum?" 'e used to ask. "What *is* night?"'

I patted her shoulder and escaped. 'Bye, Gramps.' I waved to him from his doorway. He was settling down for a nap, softly humming '*Ridi, Pagliaccio* …' under his breath.

Christine was framed in the silvery Jaguar's window like a miniature portrait, more beautiful than I remembered. She sat very straight and stared ahead of her. Her profile with its tip-tilted tiny nose and slightly parted, pouting lips was pure and heart-breaking. I tapped on the glass and she turned, startled. When she saw me, she smiled and wound down the window.

'Christine? Jack will be down soon,' I said.

'Howard? Well, hello!' She gave a tinkly laugh. 'Hilda's always talking about you.'

The car's radio was on low, playing Mozart. Was my potential new aunt cultivated? An intellectual? Leaning across the seat, she unlocked the door and patted the seat.

'Come in for a minute,' she invited.

I slid into the driver's seat. The interior smelled of leather and perfume – a money smell. Christine held out her hand and I took it awkwardly, in more of a clasp than a shake. Switching off the music, she turned to face me. Her periwinkle blue eyes were slightly surprised, honest and hurt. She was quite different from the last time I had seen her, weeping, in Hilda's flat.

'Is he still packing?' she asked. 'I wanted to go up there to help but of course I'm not allowed to. We're moving into our own flat.' Her eyes sparkled. 'Hilda found it for us. It's right next door to where she lives.'

I nodded. Her image was slowly changing before my eyes. I had always pictured her as being humbly grateful for Jack loving her. Now I saw her dignity and sense of herself. They would be a golden couple with the best of everything and I could see that she would assume her role with grace.

'What was it like up there?' she asked, her blue eyes getting more intense as she gazed at me, almost pleadingly. 'Is Mrs G having a fit?'

I shrugged. 'I think she's drunk.'

Christine giggled, her hand up to her mouth. 'Hilda's taken quite a fancy to you, Howard,' she said. 'She told me you drew her portrait.'

'Yes. I've got it here somewhere, I'll show it to you.' I rummaged in my satchel to find my sketchbook. Ruffling through the pages, I found the sketch I had done of Hilda, bright-eyed and anxious, in the café.

'But this is wonderful!' Christine cried, taking it. 'You've caught her exactly. Her expression! Oh, I must have this. I'll frame it.' Then she caught herself and apologised. 'But you won't want to ruin your book by tearing it out.'

'Oh, I don't mind.' In one careless gesture, much more careless than I actually felt, I ripped out the page.

'Thank you.' She took it. 'This is so exciting. You must sign it for me, Howard.' I found a pencil and scrawled a modest signature. Christine carefully placed the sketch on the little veneered shelf near her knees. 'What do you think about all this?' she asked.

'All what?' I asked. 'You not being Jewish?'

'Amongst other things,' she nodded. 'Jack and I moving in together, all that.'

'I don't judge people,' I said, hoping to sound very grown-up. 'And I'm not religious. I haven't set foot in a synagogue since the day of my barmitzvah. It was part of the deal.'

Christine nodded. 'Jack says you all eat bacon and ham, you all drive on Saturdays, you mix milk with meat ... all the things I'm learning you aren't allowed to do.'

'Only if you're Orthodox,' I said. 'Anyway, it's not that. It's the blood. I don't really know why.'

She nodded again. I wished I could draw the delicacy of her features at that moment. There was no getting away from it, she *was* from another race. Lighter, blonder, more transparent, as if her feelings were on the surface, clearly visible across her face as she thought them. Jewish women were darker, more maternal and solid, more secret and mysterious. It was like comparing a Picasso woman to a Fragonard lady on a swing. I could see why Jack was hopelessly in love with her – it would be like being married to a fairy – Tinker Bell, perhaps.

'Your grandfather is the nicest man in the world,' Christine suddenly said, as if to make up for the thoughts she was having about Grandma. 'He's always been so kind to me. I feel as if he's my father-in-law already. I –' she broke off to glance out at the street as if to check whether anyone was listening. 'I'm going to tell you a secret, Howard,' she decided, taking my hands. 'We're engaged. We did it secretly. Look!' She held out her ring.

I knew nothing about jewellery but I could see the diamond was large.

'It's beautiful,' I breathed. 'Congratulations, but … will you still convert?'

She nodded. 'We'll have a religious wedding in a synagogue, if that's what Mrs G wants. Meanwhile, we'll be living in sin.'

'No, it won't be sin,' I reassured her. 'We have a restaurant in Soho now. We see prostitutes walking up and down, picking up pathetic old men. That's what I call sin, not you and Jack.'

Christine burst out laughing. 'You mean it's all right as long as you're young?' she asked.

'Something like that.' I laughed too, confused. 'Anyway, I hope you'll be very happy, Christine.'

She leaned to kiss my cheek and I inhaled her delicious flowery perfume. Jack appeared a few moments later and I jumped out of the car to help him load his suitcases into the boot.

'Was it awful?' Christine asked, getting out too.

I watched them talking to each other, their hands seeking each other's hands, fingers intertwining. I had only ever seen 'love' in films and books. There was an aura about them, as if they both knew what a wonderful life lay ahead of them and how lucky they were. I envied them their happiness, but I would not have wanted their lives, not with Grandma hovering in the background like a wicked witch in a fairytale, losing no opportunity to curse them and cackle at them.

'Thank you so much for keeping me company, Howard,' Christine said as they got into the car. 'I'll treasure the portrait. Really!'

The silver Jaguar purred gently away and I made for the bus stop and the number six bus home. I vowed that I would do anything to help the beleaguered young lovers against the wicked witch.

16

A Snip, a Cut and an Extra Stitch

In the spring, my father and I were summoned to the *bris* of Frankie and Joyce's new son, Ben.

At weddings, deaths, barmitzvahs and male births, my family suddenly remembered that it was Jewish. A local rabbi would be dug up from somewhere and the males of the family would rummage through their underwear drawers in search of a *yarmulke*, the skull-cap worn out of respect for God.

Along with eight other men, Dad and I stood around in the reception of the maternity ward at a St John's Wood hospital until a matron guided us to Joyce's large private room. Joyce, pale and enormous, was resting on her bed like a beached whale. Without the orange lip-liner giving her generous lips, with her gold hair dark at the roots, she looked like a mealy-mouthed ghost. I had heard it had been a 'difficult' birth.

I bent down to kiss her and she whispered, 'Thanks for coming, Howard.'

If the baby hadn't been a boy, would we ever have got together? I doubted it. We had been invited because we made up the ten Jewish men needed for a *minyan*, the minimum for any religious ceremony.

I greeted Grandpa, who looked solemn in a Homburg hat slightly too big for him. The cousins and friends, who were all wearing hats, resembled a bunch of Broadway gangsters. The baby was lying asleep in the centre of a trolley by the window, blissfully unaware of what awaited him. A specialist in circumcision, called a *mohel*, busied himself unpacking his ghastly instruments. Out of the corner of my eye, I saw him wiping them with alcohol swabs. A blade glittered and my stomach turned. I knew I was going to be unable to look.

No women were allowed at this ceremony; even Joyce was not supposed to be present. Just another case of my family bending the rules of the Jewish religion to suit its needs. Normally, the ceremony would have been held in Joyce and Frankie's Brondesbury house, but Joyce had stayed on several days in the hospital. The uncles, subdued and serious, greeted the young rabbi when he arrived and distributed small booklets of Hebrew prayers. Waiting for the ceremony to start, the men muttering and shuffling, I realised that this was the first family occasion I had attended that was fraught with bad feeling. My father was still angry with the uncles for not wanting his investment in their business; they were equally angry that he had not wanted to invest until they were a proven success. I didn't like the way they had ignored us until they had needed ten men this morning. My father, not wanting to become an out-and-out enemy, was obliged to attend. I was kicking myself for not having included circumcisions in the deal I had made with him about not following any religion after my barmitzvah.

As the rabbi began to pray in his nasal singsong, all those Saturday mornings suffered in the synagogue came back to haunt me. No one really knew these prayers but they all pretended to, closing their eyes and swaying in time with the rabbi. A few of the more enthusiastic bent at the knees or bowed in the direction of Israel. This was known as *duvonning*. I stared at the Hebrew text and remained silent – I wasn't going to pretend. I had always been so scared of not praying, as if God himself might be watching and getting angry, but I didn't believe that any more. I glanced at the rabbi defiantly: what could he do? Throw me out?

The prayers droned on and on, interrupted only by a gurgle from the baby, who was now awake. This was the first *bris* I had seen and I hovered on the outskirts of the group of men, not wanting to see it too clearly. I watched the uncles making little *duvons* in the direction of Israel, as if they knew where it was. I suspected their minds were on impending business deals and that they were wondering how many thousands of fried eggs they could be selling.

The *mohel* carefully unwrapped the baby's nappy. I saw a glint of steel and heard an intake of breath from Uncle Frankie, who was obliged to hold his son. Although I was glad to be circumcised and felt that there was something distasteful about the uncircumcised boys I saw in the gym changing room, there was something undeniably barbaric about this cutting of a defenceless baby. A startling splash of bright blood, quickly swabbed. I looked away. When I looked back again, Frankie's ashen face told me that it had not been a pleasant sight.

A long moment of dead silence followed, which was actually the baby drawing as much breath into his tiny lungs as they could hold. Then the most piercing wail of pain I had ever heard. There was outrage and surprise in the wail: the baby was offended as well as pained. It was his first indication that the outside world might be hostile.

'*Mazeltovs*' were jovially exchanged with the father and there were more prayers, bows and knee-bends, as if this was a joyous occasion. I wanted to throw up. The baby, still howling, was wrapped and placed in its mother's arms, but Joyce's attempts to soothe him did not have the slightest effect. In fact, the cries grew louder. What that baby needed was a knock-out shot. I shook hands with Frankie, whose eyes were glazed, as if he were more shocked than the baby had been.

'Did I go through all this?' I whispered to my father.

'Not exactly.' He accepted a tiny glass of wine from the rabbi, indicating that I should take one too. 'We were in Berkshire when you were born. There were no rabbis around, so we had to ask a butcher.'

'A *butcher*?' I gasped.

'He was a kosher butcher,' my father assured me. I nodded, feeling as depersonalised as a sausage.

Joyce darted looks up at Frankie, as if seeking his approval for having borne him a son. She declined the wine, but the men began clinking glasses and crying:

'*L'chayyim*! To life!' Blood and wine, I thought miserably. That's religion! There was a sense of relief when the rabbi and his *mohel* left, pocketing the envelopes Frankie passed to them. I wondered what a poor man did if he had a son.

The baby's cries began to level off into whimpers. Each time I thought of what he must be feeling, I had to squeeze my legs together.

Frankie tossed a small package onto Joyce's bed. It had a Hatton Gardens jeweller's label on it. Joyce gave a cry of surprise and ripped off the paper, snapping open the box. Nestled against purple velvet was a brooch in the shape of a branch with diamond flowers and leaves. She pulled Frankie down to kiss her thanks and proudly pinned the brooch to her bed-jacket. A Jewish husband traditionally gave his wife a piece of 'good' jewellery to thank her for a son. It was rumoured, half-jokingly, that a Jewish husband also slipped his wife's surgeon a hundred pounds with instructions to put in a couple of extra stitches after the birth. I overheard a couple of Whitechapel cousins sniggering, but did not fully understand. In my innocence, I imagined it was something to do with urination.

'In two years she'll get a mink coat,' my father murmured. It seemed demeaning, this idea of little rewards along the way for services rendered. But Joyce was smiling, her eyes alive for the first time that day.

'Isn't it gorgeous?' she asked me, indicating the brooch. 'It's just as well it was a boy, because this'll be the last one.' She rolled her eyes at me. 'I'm not putting myself through that again, Howard.'

'Was it that bad?' I asked.

'Don't even ask!' She shuddered. 'You're lucky you're a man.'

'Really? Look what men have to suffer.' I indicated the baby, still softly sobbing himself to sleep in her arms.

She glanced down at him. 'Poor Benny.' She patted him. 'But he'll forget it ever happened.'

This event left a faintly unsavoury taste in my mouth. The religious ceremony, the cutting, the screams of pain and the diamond brooch. Frankie's offhand treatment of his wife had spread to the cousins, who, apart from a brief nod of 'Hello', had barely acknowledged her. We should have been sitting on the bed, chatting to her, but nobody did that. When we left a few minutes later, I took big grateful gulps of the fresh air of St John's Wood, kissed Grandpa goodbye and watched the uncles hustle him into a big car to be sped to the Oxford Street Egg. They had not thanked us for coming.

It was Saturday morning and my Saturday mornings had changed. I now drove with my father to Soho and helped him set up the tables and chairs, after sweeping the floor. I wandered the streets, poking my nose into book-stores and newsagents, timing the odd prostitute's session, and lingering outside St Martin's School of Art, just to get the feel of it. Then I drank cappuccino until just before lunchtime and my cashier duty.

*

My mother finally found a new maid. Her name was May and she was ten years older than our usual maids. Respectable and straitlaced, she had won third place in the Miss Ireland ballroom-dancing contest two years previously, and still carried the cutting from the *Irish Times* in her handbag. May was calm and efficient and had her life all planned out. She intended to marry within four years. She just needed to find the man. My mother taught her how to turn Irish stew into Jewish food by substituting kosher meat and adding a few bay leaves. May turned the maid's room into a cosy place, which I often visited to sit on her bed and talk to her. I sketched her as she leafed through her *Woman's Realm*.

*

It was three months since Jack had moved out. Grandma was attempting to pick up the shattered pieces of her life. Now that my mother had stopped attending the Friday night dinners, and we had all followed suit, she was faced with the company only of her daughter-in-law Joyce, Barbara and little Benny. Jack and Christine were, of course, not welcome. They would have destroyed the main topic of conversation. Gradually, cousins, aunts, friends and cronies swelled the numbers. This provided an excuse to cook enormous dinners, which took Grandma's mind off her son.

In Grandma's opinion, only the butchers she had known in her Whitechapel childhood could provide decent meat and chicken. She had never warmed to the Edgware Road butchers, even if they were kosher. Perhaps this was an excuse to visit Whitechapel each week on a long bus ride and meditate on her progress from East to West End. Early on Friday mornings, she caught the number six bus to Aldgate. There was a long walk to the butcher, but this only added to the sacrifice Grandma made for family and friends. She would stock up on the chickens and meat which fed the family for a week, returning on the same route, dragging two heavy 'shoppers' and delicately holding a small plastic bag of unhatched yolks, bright yellow in their red-veined membranes. These turned up in her chicken soup as tiny, powdery, pale yellow orbs. They were considered a great delicacy and it was a matter of pride that she broke none on her journey home.

The poorer part of the family still lived in Whitechapel, including Grandma's sister Sarah who had not wanted to 'better herself' and had chosen to stay on in her modest, terraced house. Unbelievably, for the first twelve years of my life, Grandma had had a mother too. She was a tiny, walnut-wrinkled sparrow of a woman who spoke not a word of English and clucked lovingly over us, presenting us with an orange at the end of our infrequent visits.

'Why did she give us an orange, Mum?' we would whine when we got home, tossing them ungratefully into the fruit bowl.

'Because when she was a little girl, oranges were a great treat,' my mother would explain.

She was our Bubba, and when she died a few months after my barmitzvah, her death was carefully hidden from us. Thus it was that later, when one of us idly enquired, 'Why don't we visit Bubba anymore?' we were told that she had died months ago. That was the way deaths were treated in our family.

She had lived in a small, dark Aldgate street and had never wanted to move. Grandma's roots were still very much there and she felt entirely at home, four months after her new grandson's birth, as she took her place in the queue of women waiting to be served, her feet firmly planted on the sawdust-covered floor. Mary was with her that day to help with the heavy bags. It was a sunny Friday, the busiest day at the shop as women bought their weekend joints and Friday night chickens. Grandma glanced around the crowd to see if there was anyone she knew. A woman who looked vaguely familiar smiled at her, so Grandma nodded.

''Allo, 'ow are you?'

The woman said, '*Mazeltov*, Mrs G.' It was quite normal for people to know Grandma's name even when she had no idea of theirs. She was almost a local celebrity, her nails and jewels famous from her visits to her mother and sister.

'That was weeks ago,' Grandma laughed. 'My little grandson's at 'ome now.'

'Yes?' The woman edged nearer. 'And it must be lovely to have another one on the way?'

'What other one, what are you talkin' about?' Grandma asked. 'There's only one. Little Ben. 'E was named after my mother, Bella.'

'I didn't mean that grandchild, Mrs G,' the woman insisted. 'The other one! The one your other son's going to have. What *nacchus*, eh?'

Nacchus was the Jewish word for the pleasure your children give you. There was a sudden silence in the buzzing crowd and, as Grandma suddenly understood, her face went black.

'What *nacchus*, eh?' the woman tried again, smiling evilly.

Mary nudged Grandma, willing her to stay calm. The two women were attuned to each other and quick-witted.

Grandma pretended to go a little vague, nodding her head and murmuring, 'Mmmm, nice ...' and beginning a conference about meat cuts with Mary as a smoke-screen to give her time to think. Out of the corner of her eye she sized up the woman who had been so eager to deliver this devastating news, in public, and at the butcher's. This woman must be an enemy, one who knew only too well that *nacchus* was the very last word for a son expecting a baby with his unmarried *shiksa*. Still talking to Mary about how many guests they expected for dinner that evening, Grandma focused all her power on the woman, who began to fidget uncomfortably under the scrutiny. She lowered her eyes in confusion and studied her shopping-list. Grandma triumphantly placed her. She was the neighbour of her sister, who lived nearby, and she had once pushed her incredibly ugly daughter onto Jack in an effort to marry her off. Jack had recoiled from the girl, who had a moustache, and it hadn't done Grandma's cause much good. This had produced the enmity: a rejected girl's mother's revenge.

Grandma nodded, almost pleased. Now that she had placed this creature, she could deal with her. First, she bought her meat, almost automatically, turning down one chicken in favour of a plumper one, making sure she got her full quota of unhatched yolks wrapped in a separate bag. She bade the butcher goodbye.

When the woman had the effrontery to say, 'Goodbye, Mrs G,' Grandma pounced.

'Is your daughter married yet?' she asked, silencing the shop. The woman flinched slightly but stood her ground, smiling uneasily.

'No, Mrs G, not yet. You know how fussy girls are these days.'

'Tell 'er not to be *too* fussy.' Grandma smiled grimly. 'I'll 'ave a little talk with 'er one day, if you'd like. About electrolysis.'

She sailed out, feeling that she had won that round. With Mary glancing fearfully at her as she trotted along, they reached the bus stop in silence. Only when she was aboard the bus, wedged in against the wall next to Mary, did Grandma speak.

'Did you 'ear what she said?' she asked in a low voice.

Mary burst out in a torrent of breathlessness. 'Sure I did, Mrs G, but don't take on so, yet. She might have been making it up. You know what people are like round here. Sometimes to get at you, people say the wickedest things, sure.'

'Makin' it up?' Grandma drew herself up. 'Why would she do such a thing? Makin' it up? What good would it do *'er*? No! She was tellin' the truth. My son's goin' to give me a bastard. Oooh, Mary.' She clutched at her heart. 'I think I'm going to faint.'

'Well, I'm glad you waited until we got on the bus, Mrs G.' Mary fished in her bag for smelling salts. 'Here.' She nudged Grandma with the bottle. 'Take a sniff now. Don't go jumping to conclusions.'

Grandma pushed the salts away. 'What conclusions, what are you talkin' about?' she snapped. 'If a young man starts livin' with a young woman, you don't need no conclusions. Sooner or later, they're goin' to 'ave a little bastard, aren't they?'

Mary glanced around the bus. 'Don't call the wee small thing that, Mrs G,' she pleaded. 'Not before the poor mite's even been born. Sure, it's through no fault of the child.'

Grandma changed her mind and took a small sniff of the smelling salts. Her head jerked back and she fanned herself with one hand, giving a silencing glare at Mary. It didn't work.

'Sure, they must still have plenty of time to get married?' Mary gasped.

'What are you talking about – married?' Grandma cried.

She stopped suddenly, staring at Mary as the penny dropped. If they didn't marry, they would present her with a bastard. If they didn't marry, Christine would not convert to Judaism, and the child would be born Christian. She turned to stare out of the bus window, not opening her mouth until they reached the Edgware Road.

The two women got off the bus near Marks and Spencer, lugging the heavy bags. As usual, the bag containing the unhatched egg-yolks was carried delicately, separately from the rest, by Grandma. She had had nearly an hour to think on the slow bus ride. When they reached the flat, she poured herself a shot of whisky. After a moment, she poured a second one for Mary – after all, she had been a terrific support. What would she have done without her? Mary was unpacking the chickens, laying them out on the draining board for Grandma to prepare. Grandma sniffed, setting the whisky down next to Mary.

'We've both 'ad a shock,' she said, to justify the drink.

She walked down the corridor to the telephone by the front door. Swallowing the whisky, she looked up the number of the Egg & I. She had her husband paged.

'Max?' she said when she heard his voice. 'Come 'ome.'

'What is it? Are you ill?'

'No, I'm fine. It's about our son.'

'What about him? I just saw him ten minutes ago.'

'Did 'e tell you 'e's going to give us a little bastard?'

'No! No, we were talking about egg deliveries.'

'Well, this is an egg delivery you wasn't expectin', Max! Our son's *shiksa* is goin' to give us the first bastard we've 'ad in our family. Nice news, that, isn't it? Oh, Max!' She began to wail. 'What did I do to deserve this? Didn't I always teach 'im right from wrong? Two such 'andsome boys with everything in front of them, and now 'e's throwin' away 'is life like this.'

'Don't start drinking,' Grandpa said.

'With all I went through for the both of them, didn't I deserve –'

'Have you been drinking?' Grandpa asked, sharply.

'Didn't I give them all the love and attention a mother –'

'I'm asking you a question! Have you started drinking?'

She waited a moment. 'I needed a drink, Max,' she said. 'I would 'ave passed out otherwise. I needed smellin' salts on the bus 'ome. Thank God I 'ad Mary with me. If it wasn't for Mary, I'd be –' she broke off to splutter a small sob. 'I 'ad to 'ave a stranger tell me, Max. Someone I don't even know – a proper *yuchna* – at the butcher's. In front of all those people. Oh, Max, I've never been so ashamed.'

'Well, stop drinking right now, okay? We're in the middle of the lunch-hour here, it's very busy. I'll leave early. I don't want to find you *shicke* when I get home.'

Grandma took a deep breath. 'I'll be *shicke* if I want! I'll be under the *table* if I feel like it! A mother who's done what I've done for them boys? If I can't 'ave a little drink to 'elp me through it – so 'elp me God – I'll run out into the street and *scream*! You want me to do that?'

There was a long pause during which she could hear the chatter and clatter of the busy restaurant. Then Grandpa muttered: 'Do what you want,' and hung up.

''Ung up on me,' she announced to Mary. 'My own 'usband.'

Mary grunted, consulting her watch. 'Sure, it's after one, he must be very busy there,' she said. Grandma poured a full tumbler of whisky for herself and quickly gulped some down.

''E's not goin' to be no 'elp, Mary,' she said mournfully. 'No 'elp at all.' She sat down heavily. 'There'll be murders tonight when 'e gets 'ome,' she predicted.

'Don't take it out on Mr G,' Mary pleaded. 'Sure it's not the man's fault, all this.'

'What are you talkin' about?' Grandma demanded, her eyes open wide. 'Of *course* it's 'is fault. It's *all* 'is fault.'

*

Three hours later, the spotless kitchen, usually abuzz with frantic cooking on a Friday evening, was silent and cold. The plucked chickens, still smelling of singed feathers, lay on the draining-board awaiting their pummelling into the delicious *gedempt* chicken that Grandma was famous for. The chickens showed no sign of getting *gedempt*, however, and Grandma was in no hurry to *gedempt* them. Sitting at the kitchen table, pondering her choices, she slowly came to realise that the main problem was that there weren't any choices. She could not cut her favourite son out of her life. The problem was how to come out looking like a winner.

*

Grandpa arrived home at five o'clock, sniffing the cooking-free air suspiciously. He took one look at Grandma and the unused kitchen and left for the barber's, a day early, where he requested 'the works'. That would use up at least two hours, including the hot steamy towel wrapped lovingly around his head and left there as he dozed off, dreaming of some tropical paradise.

And then … either Mary had bumped into someone, or Grandpa relayed the news from the barber's chair, but somehow people knew they should stay away that Friday night. By bush telegram or jungle drum, the cronies, cousins and hangers-on seemed to know that the chickens were not going to get *gedempt*, the soup not simmered, the large white table cloth not spread out on the usually welcoming dining table. Everyone knew but me, that is. Unusually, uniquely, on that evening I was heading for Grandma's and what I thought was going to be dinner with the family.

17

''E Didn't Invite 'Is Own Mother
to the Wedding'

I had not eaten Friday night dinner at Grandma's since
the rift had begun. But I made myself quite an appetite for
gedempt chicken and decided that I must be the one to
bridge the gap.

Something made me drop in on Hilda first.

'Howard! What a lovely surprise.' Hilda threw open the
door of her flat, eyes sparkling, a wide smile on her face.
'Have you come to congratulate me? I'm just off to
Christine's. We're all having dinner tonight, come with
me?'

I waited while she gathered up some heavy plastic bags
from the kitchen and pulled on a raincoat. Her hair and
make-up were neat and fresh and she had added two
dangling earrings, giving her a festive air.

On the way downstairs she laughed. 'This isn't nearly as
shocking as it seems, Howard. Christine will explain.' I
wondered what on earth she was talking about.

The neighbouring building was a replica of Hilda's. She
jabbed a bell and pushed the front door: it was open.

'Hilda? Is that you?' Christine's voice called down.

'Yes. I've got Howard with me,' Hilda called. She sailed
up the steep flight with her usual energy. I dragged along
behind.

'Howard!' Christine greeted me at the top of the stairs.
'I'm so pleased to see you. You'll be one of the first to
know.'

She hugged me and I inhaled her flowery perfume. They ushered me into a flat that smelled freshly painted. The rooms were carpeted and the furniture new. Although it was pleasant and comfortable, it seemed as anonymous as a hotel suite.

'You don't know, do you?' Christine held me at arm's length. She was glowing, her eyes full of mischief. She had never seemed so beautiful. 'Look at his face, Hilda,' she laughed. 'He doesn't know what this is all about.'

'So put the poor boy out of his misery!' Hilda cried.

Christine held out her hand, palm down. 'Look, Howard! Isn't it beautiful?'

I stared at the glittering diamond.

'Is that why you came, dear?' Hilda asked. 'Did you just hear?'

'You married?' I frowned. 'When?'

'Three months ago,' Christine said. 'Your uncle's a very old-fashioned, strait-laced man. Remember what we said about living in sin? Well, Jack had no intention of living in sin. We went to Marylebone Register Office the day after he moved in. It was very private. Only Hilda and my father –'

'They'll have a proper wedding later,' Hilda said, pouring sherry into glasses. 'Right now you must toast the bride.'

'And I've got even better news,' Christine cried.

'What?' I asked.

'We're having a baby,' Christine said. 'It's due in March. Oh, Howard, I'm so happy.' She hugged me again as I tried to absorb all this news.

'Your uncle will be here soon and we'll have a lovely dinner. Please stay,' Hilda said. 'I've done a roast, and I shouldn't be surprised if I got quite merry. It's not as if I have a long journey home.'

'I was on my way to Grandma's,' I explained, taking the sherry. 'I thought I'd have dinner there.'

'I shouldn't think there'll be much to eat up there, tonight,' Hilda said, giggling. 'Not if I know your Grandma.'

'Stay here with us,' Christine begged. 'We're much more fun.'

'No, maybe he should go,' Hilda said thoughtfully. 'He could come back and tell us what's going on.'

'Hilda!' Christine was shocked. 'Don't turn poor Howard into a spy. We don't need another one. Mary already tells us everything.'

Hilda poured more sherry. 'I don't mean to be disrespectful to your grandmother, dear, but really, this couldn't have worked out better if we'd planned it.' She sipped her sherry. 'She *has* to approve of Christine now.'

'First babies are often late,' Christine said thoughtfully. 'I'll try to complete my Jewish studies. With any luck, I'll be Jewish before the birth.'

'The main thing is, they're married,' Hilda exulted. 'And there's nothing Mrs G can do to spoil this now.'

In her triumph, Hilda clinked my glass with hers and spilled some sherry. 'Oooh,' she squealed, looking for a cloth. 'Don't worry, it's good for the carpet.'

I watched them fussing around, feeling alarmed. There was a lot Grandma could do to spoil things. Didn't they realise how powerful she was?

I walked the few hundred yards to Grandma's flat as it grew dark and people hurried home from work. A few drops of rain fell. A 'wash-out summer' was being predicted. Grandpa opened the door to me, his face pink, reeking of barbershop cologne.

'You've been to the barber's?' I asked.

He winked at me, lowering his voice as we walked towards the kitchen. 'If I have to suffer tonight, I thought I might as well be well-groomed. I stocked up on cigars too.' He tapped his shirt pocket. Bending towards me, he whispered, 'She's very aggravated. Refused to cook any dinner.'

'Stop mutterin' to 'im out there and come into the kitchen,' Grandma's voice rang out. Grandpa looked at me meaningfully. 'Gets on my nerves to 'ear that mutterin' goin' on.'

I walked into the brightly-lit kitchen and found Grandma sitting at the table, studying her nails.

'Give your Grandma a kiss, darlin',' she said.

I bent to kiss her. Although she smelled of whisky, I had never seen her so sober.

'Don't know why you chose tonight to come 'ere,' she said. 'It won't be much of a dinner. I 'ave to put my 'eart and soul into my cooking and I didn't feel like it today. Not after 'earin' *that* news.'

She looked full into my face and I noticed her eyes – a washed-out grey, as if tears had drained their colour.

'I can't cry anymore and drinking doesn't seem to be doing me much good,' she shrugged, surprised. 'I don't know what's going to 'appen to me.'

I sat down, pulling my chair towards her. 'Can't you be happy for them?' I asked. I decided not to mention that I had just been there. 'They must be very happy.'

She looked at me. 'Really?' she said, trying to sound sarcastic. 'I've never 'eard of a son bein' 'appy at killin' 'is mother. Funny things make people 'appy, I suppose.'

She got to her feet and opened the door of the fridge. 'Left-overs!' she announced. 'I'll warm something up.'

It was odd sitting in the kitchen on a Friday night, just my grandparents and me. The phone did not ring and the doorbell stayed silent. I was glad I had come, for Grandpa's sake, but it was the worst meal I had ever eaten there. I wasn't even sure what it was – meat and vegetables, stewed beyond recognition. It was hard to swallow, but Grandpa seemed determined to eat heartily, pretending to find it delicious.

At one point, he urged, 'Have a little something.'

And Grandma said, 'I can't.'

Dessert was as bleak: Grandpa carefully peeled an apple and offered me half. Afterwards he lit up his cigar, obviously the part of the meal he had been looking forward to, and we moved to the room with the television to watch the News. Out of consideration for Grandma, who mechanically followed us, Grandpa kept the volume low. I shot little glances at Grandma, seated at the far end of the long dining table, which on any other Friday night would have seated some fifteen guests. She had poured herself more whisky and sipped at it, her lower lip jutting rebelliously. She lit a cigarette and smoked it, slowly.

'Can you imagine,' she suddenly asked us, 'the butcher's? Before all those women? *That's* where I 'ad to hear this news.' She stared at Grandpa, who stared at the television. ''E couldn't come to me 'ere, in my own 'ome, and say, "Ma? We're goin' to 'ave a little bastard. After all you've done for me, we're going to give you the joy and the respect and the *nacchus* of 'avin' the first little bastard in the family." '

'Okay,' Grandpa grunted. 'We get the message. Can we change the subject and talk about something else now?'

'Oh, yes!' Grandma put a sickly grin on her face. 'What would you like to talk about? Should we talk about the weather?'

She got to her feet, a little unsteadily, and went to the windows behind the couch. Flinging them wide open, she signalled to her husband.

'Come 'ere. I'll talk about the weather with you.'

Grandpa stood up too, looking at her disapprovingly. 'You're drunk,' he stated. Stubbing out his half-smoked cigar, he stalked from the room.

I stood now, but before I could make my goodbyes, Grandma gave an angry snort and ran towards me. Grabbing my hand, she pulled me, with amazing force, around the sofa to the windows. It was raining and the cold air came rushing in – a contrast to the tropical heat of the flat. Grandma's face, lit orange by a nearby street-lamp, was twisted. Did she intend to hurl herself out? Or me? With my wrist in her grip, she pushed me so close to the sill I could feel the rain on my face.

'*Tell* them!' she commanded. 'I want everyone in the street to know what a son can do to a mother.'

There was no one in the wet street. I turned away.

'Grandma …' I said reprovingly.

She pushed me back to the window. 'Come on! Nice an' clear! Tell them your Uncle Jack's going to give 'is mother a little bastard! I want them to know!' She glared at me, her face screwed up with expectation.

'Grandma, aren't you being a little –'

'*Tell* them!' she yelled, wrenching my arm. 'Do it! Say, "My Uncle Jack's givin' 'is mother a little bastard." ' She had always been good at getting me to do things I had no intention of doing. In the normal world. As her eyes bulged alarmingly, I felt I should perhaps humour her. I was afraid of her.

'Uncle Jack's going to give his mother a bastard,' I muttered.

'*Louder.*' She punched me, her eyes wild. 'Much louder than that! So everyone in the street can hear.'

'My Uncle Jack's going to give his mother a bastard,' I cried out. I had never felt so stupid. My face was flushed with cowardice and embarrassment. The rain pelted down and Grandma gazed with some satisfaction into the street.

'That's right,' she nodded, 'a little bastard.' Her eyes glittered as one or two windows opposite lit up. 'Now get your grandfather. *He* has to tell them too.'

'Isn't it enough that *I've* told them?' I groaned. 'He's probably asleep.'

'*Get* 'im!'

She shoved me so hard that I nearly fell down. She was all puffed up with emotion, her breast high, her mouth set in a line. The whisky had hit her. In the reflected light from the street-lamp, her eyes shone orange.

I ran to my grandfather's bedroom. 'Grandpa?' I gently shook his shoulder. He was lying on the white satin bedspread, drifting into a snooze. 'Grandpa, I'm sorry to disturb you but I think you ought to come and help Grandma. She seems to be having – I don't know – some kind of funny turn. I think she's drunk.'

'For God's sake.' He sat up with a groan, swinging his legs over the side of the bed.

Taking my shoulder, he hauled himself to his feet, stuck his feet into his slippers and shuffled after me. I led him down the corridor into the dining room. Grandma was still leaning out of the window.

'Max?' She turned eagerly to him. ''Oward just told the

neighbours that my next grandchild is going to be a little *goy* bastard. Now I want *you* to tell them.'

Grandpa looked coolly at her, his eyes narrowing. 'Go to hell,' he said evenly.

'I want you to lean out and tell 'em that after all I've done for 'im, 'e's goin' to give me a –'

'Close the bloody windows!' Grandpa told her.

I had never heard him swear before.

'Very nice,' Grandma nodded grimly, almost pleased. 'A very nice thing to say to your wife.'

Fat tears rolled down her cheeks as she stared helplessly at him. A gust of wind brought a shower of rain into the room.

'I said close the bloody windows!' Grandpa roared.

He jabbed me in the ribs, as if I should close them. Perhaps he wanted to hit out at Grandma, but I was closer. I approached Grandma nervously; they were a dangerous couple to get between. I pulled the windows shut and drew the curtains. My grandparents stood frozen, glaring at each other.

'You're losing your senses,' Grandpa said. 'Our youngest son's going to be a father and all you can think of is nasty words. Bastard? Is that a nice thing to call your grandchild?'

Grandma glared at him. 'Well, it *will* be a bastard, won't it?' she asked. 'A little bastard. Isn't that what they call children whose parents aren't married?'

I couldn't bear it anymore. 'They *are* married, Grandma,' I blurted out. 'They married in a register office three months ago.'

Grandma sat on the arm of the sofa, her head bowed. 'A son,' she marvelled quietly, tears pouring down her face. 'A son gets married and doesn't invite 'is own mother. It'll be a *goy*.' She looked up. 'My own grandchild a *yock*. *Goy* blood running through its veins.'

'They'll marry in a synagogue,' I told her. 'She's studying with a rabbi.'

'What good will that do?' Grandma muttered, staring from me to Grandpa and back again. 'I'll be dead by the time they reach the synagogue. They'll 'ave killed me.'

'You won't be dead,' Grandpa told her. 'You'll be there, under the *chuppah*, all dressed up, as proud as any mother.'

Grandma got to her feet, suddenly energised. 'I'm going round there *now*!' she announced. She pulled at my arm. 'Come on, you're taking me.' She swept out of the room to find her coat and umbrella.

I looked at Grandpa. He made a little gesture with his hand. 'Go with her,' he nodded. 'Let's have an end to all this *mischegas*. My nerves can't take anymore.'

*

It was raining heavily when we reached the street. A strong wind blew the rain into our faces and nearly turned the umbrella inside out. Grandma didn't notice. Possibly she would have welcomed a snowstorm to add another element of nature to be overcome. No one was out in this weather, although music and laughter came from an Irish pub on the corner. My mind was fixed on just when I could escape and go home. Grandma hurried along beside me in the rain, holding my arm to balance herself on the slippery wet pavement. I felt as if I were caught in the claw of an eagle, one of her nails digging into me and drawing, I was sure, blood. But I did not dare complain. We reached the modest doorway and I glanced at my watch. It was just after ten o'clock.

'Isn't it a bit late?' I tried.

'Don't worry, they'll be in,' Grandma cried.

Indicating the bell, I said, 'That's their flat.'

'Well?' Grandma stared at me. 'Aren't you goin' to ring it?'

I rang, and made as if to disentangle myself from her grip, muttering, 'Well, I'll be going now –'

Her grip on my arm tightened. 'You're comin' in with me,' she announced. 'You 'ave to introduce me.'

'To your son?' I asked, hoping to lighten the mood with a joke.

Grandma remained stony-faced. 'No, not to my son, don't be so clever! To my daughter-in-law. That's what she is now, isn't she?'

It was the first time she'd referred to Christine as anything other than 'the *shiksa*': was it a good sign?

'Who is it?' Jack's voice sounded from behind the door.

'Uncle Jack, it's me, Howard. I'm with Grandma.' He opened the door.

'Is *this* what you wanted?' Grandma cried. Jack stood just inside the door, staring at her. 'You want to kill me?' She indicated her wet shoulders and hair. ''Appy now? Draggin' me out in the middle of the night to catch my death of cold? When I'm *dead*, will you be 'appy?'

Jack swallowed. 'Are you coming up?' he asked uncertainly. He turned to lead the way.

I let Grandma pass ahead up the steep flight. It seemed to take hours to reach the top and an odd logic told me to allow her ahead of me so that if she fell, she would fall on me, softening her fall but killing me. She held onto the banister, hauling herself up and finally reached the top, wet and breathless.

'Is this what you wanted?' she panted. 'Why didn't you find a flat on the top floor so you could kill me?'

Jack's face was expressionless. 'Come in and meet Christine,' he said. 'We can drink to the health of our child.'

Grandma took a deep breath and hoisted her proud bosom. She plastered a big false smile on her face and sailed into the flat. She must have wanted them to realise the smile was fake since she could just as easily put a real smile on her lips. Christine appeared, her blue eyes wide with apprehension, her smile nervous. She wore a pretty lavender dress with a white cardigan draped over her shoulders. Jack's arm went protectively around her. Grandma nudged me.

'Oh yes, Grandma … this is Christine. Christine, this is … your mother-in-law,' I said.

I stood back, waiting for an explosion but, although Grandma drew herself up even higher, it was as if she had come under some strange spell as she regarded – no, scrutinised – Christine.

'Beautiful,' she whispered, shaking her head. 'Blonde, slim, like a film star.' For a moment, she seemed lost in admiration, as though she had fallen in love with Christine herself, instead of Jack. Then she snapped herself out of it and barked, 'What? There weren't enough *Christian* men for you?'

She held out an imperious hand on which she had remembered to plant her largest diamond ring. Christine glanced at the hand for a moment, then darted forward and pecked Grandma's cheek. Grandma remained upright, unmoving.

'That's right,' Jack said, moving us into the warm living room where a chocolate cake cut into portions was still on the table, along with some half-empty wine glasses. There was no sign of Hilda; she must have either left early or passed out.

'Here, Mrs G.' Christine handed her a glass Jack had poured. 'Let's propose a toast and bury the hatchet, what do you say?'

''Atchet?' Grandma's eyes widened. 'I 'aven't got no 'atchet. I've only come 'ere to remind my son of 'is duty.'

'And what's that?' Jack asked, surprisingly stern. He was holding Christine before him like a shield.

Grandma's eyes narrowed slightly. 'If you really loved your parents, you'd get rid of this baby,' she said. 'There's ways of doin' it. She could drink a 'ole bottle of gin and take a very 'ot bath. She could –'

'We're going to pretend we didn't hear that, Mrs G,' Christine cut her off, smiling a pleasant smile. 'We wouldn't dream of destroying this baby.'

'We're planning a lot more,' Jack said.

'Oh, my God!' Grandma took a sudden gulp of wine and collapsed into the nearest armchair, clutching her heart. Christine regarded her calmly.

'I don't understand, you have such a wonderful family,' she told Grandma. 'Your husband's always been so nice to me. Do you mind if I suggest something, Mrs G?'

Grandma stared at her dazedly and Christine gave a nervous little laugh. 'Why don't you just relax and *enjoy* your family instead of making their lives difficult? I have my father's blessing. I'm sure Mr G would give us his blessing too.'

Grandma let out a bitter laugh. 'Oh, 'e'd give anyone 'is blessing, 'e would,' she cackled. ''E'd be 'appy if 'is sons married *black* girls.'

Christine's smile froze. 'I'm studying to be Jewish,' she said.

'I don't believe in mixed marriages,' Grandma stated. 'They don't last. A Jewish marriage is 'ard enough, believe me, the way the men are.' She gave Christine a dark look.

'If two people really love each other, Mrs G,' Christine began, 'the way Jack and I do –'

'We've never 'ad no bastard in our family,' Grandma pointed out. 'I didn't go through all I've been through to be told in some butcher's shop that my son's giving me a bastard.'

Jack choked on his wine. 'It won't be a bastard, Ma,' he said. 'We're married.'

'Married?' Grandma's voice cracked in surprise. 'Well, well, isn't that nice.' Tears spurted from her eyes. She shot me a look to shut me up. 'And when was this?'

'Three months ago,' Jack said. 'The day we moved in together. We'll have another wedding in a synagogue, once Christine's converted. The baby will be officially Jewish.'

Grandma dabbed at her eyes. 'I've never 'eard of a son getting married without invitin' 'is mother,' she cried softly.

'It wasn't much of a wedding, Mrs G,' Christine soothed her. 'We'd love to have you and Mr G at the proper one, in a synagogue, with –'

'With all your belly stickin' out?' Grandma cried. 'A lovely bride *you'll* make!'

'You know the people to get her through quickly,' Jack urged.

'I could be Jewish before I really start to show,' Christine suggested. They fell silent, watching Grandma.

Grandma gave Christine another thorough scrutiny.

'So slim,' she marvelled, shaking her head. 'Such a lovely girl. You must 'ave 'ad a 'undred men after you. Why *my* son?'

'What d'you say, Ma?' Jack prodded her. 'Christine has other things to do with her time – we'd only be doing this to please you. If you don't care whether she converts or not –'

'Her father won't be allowed under the *chuppah*,' Grandma warned.

'A wedding canopy,' Jack explained for Christine's benefit. 'The wedding party stands under it during the ceremony.'

'You can't stand under it if you're not Jewish,' Grandma stated. 'I don't suppose your father will be converting, will he?'

'Not if it's just to stand under a canopy.' Christine frowned, trying to stay patient.

'Any baby you have must be named after my mother, you know,' Grandma said.

'These are just details, Ma,' Jack said. 'We'll do all that. Just as long as Christine is happy, I'm happy.'

'And I always knew I'd only be happy with Jack,' Christine avowed. 'It's that simple.'

The couple joined hands tightly and Grandma glanced down at them.

'I'm glad you think it's so simple,' she said, sourly. 'I don't think it's so simple, throwin' away your life like that.'

'Oh, Mrs G.' Christine fell to her knees and took Grandma's hands. 'We're not throwing away our lives. How can you say such a thing?'

Grandma disentangled her hands from Christine's and stood up, wobbling slightly.

'I want to speak with my son,' she said. 'In private!' Jack shrugged and took his mother into the bedroom.

I helped Christine to her feet and she poured us some wine. We exchanged glances.

'Poor Jack,' I sympathised.

'Oh, don't worry about him.' Christine sat down. 'In his own quiet way, he's as stubborn as your grandmother.'

We sat on the sofa together, listening to the shrill squawks of Grandma and the answering monotonous bass of Jack, but without understanding any words.

'It is very simple,' Christine declared. 'She can either have nothing to do with us, or make the best of it and stay on friendly terms.'

18

Ciao, Vito!

'She'll make the best of it,' my mother said, lighting up her first cigarette after breakfast the next morning. 'I can't picture her disowning her precious son. Anyway, the moment she sees a new grandchild, she'll forget Christine isn't Jewish.'

I watched her, a little disappointed that she wasn't as scandalised by my account of the previous evening as I'd thought she'd be. She smoked thoughtfully, watching Lawrence cycle around the back garden.

'Is Dad still asleep?' I asked her. It was nearly nine o'clock.

She nodded. 'He can't take the pace,' she told me. 'We stayed open until two. I could have worked until four. We took over two hundred pounds. I *love* working!'

She stubbed out her cigarette and stood up, bending to give me a quick hug. I could feel the energy coiled inside her. She was wearing one of her new, bright dresses, a wide belt cinching in her slim waist. She preferred to buy six new cheap dresses rather than one good one.

'This weekend will be busy too,' she told me, gathering the breakfast dishes. 'We've got a five-shilling minimum now. They won't be allowed to nurse a cappuccino for two hours. It makes Dad so irritable. They come in and smoke and read!'

'Isn't that what coffee bars are for?' I asked.

'Not if you're the owner,' Mum said, plonking the kettle onto a fiery gas ring. 'I don't mind if they sit and read up at the bar. I just can't bear to see a table for four going to waste.' She poured a cup of tea and took it upstairs to Dad.

Rachel wandered down in night-gown and robe a few minutes later. 'They've taken on a new dreamboat of a waiter,' she whispered, on her way to the kitchen. 'His name's Vito. Short for Vittorio …' She said his name in a swoony voice. 'He's gorgeous. Dad's going to be jealous again. He's Italian, of course, and he stares at Mum with these big bedroom eyes.'

'What are bedroom eyes?' I asked tetchily, resenting Rachel knowing a term I hadn't come across in Freud. She giggled.

'Eyes that undress you and *drag* you into the bedroom,' she breathed. 'Mum goes all funny when Vito's around.'

'Oh, don't be so silly,' I snapped.

Rachel took toast from the grill and buttered it, bringing it into the room where we ate.

'Italians know how to make a woman feel so appreciated,' she said authoritatively, taking a bite of toast. She edged nearer, lowering her voice. '*I've* got an Italian boyfriend! His name's Roberto. He's got a little Vespa and he takes me for rides around Soho. He goes so fast I have to cling to his back as if I'm hugging him. I'm so in love I could die!'

I stared at her in dismay. 'Oh, this is vomit-making,' I said, grimacing.

'They'd *never* let me marry him,' Rachel sighed. 'He's so un-Jewish, it's not even funny.'

'Uncle Jack's married a non-Jewish girl,' I let drop casually.

This time I got the reaction I sought. Rachel's mouth opened, full of half-chewed toast. I recounted the previous night's events.

'Roberto would never convert.' She shook her head when I had finished. 'He's *proud* of being a Catholic. He wears a *crucifix*, for Christ's sake. Sometimes he crosses himself!'

'How?' I blurted out in spite of myself.

Rachel made the sign of the cross for me and we stared at each other gravely. This was grown-up stuff and I was out of my depth. I felt fiercely jealous of Rachel moving beyond my sphere and into the adult world. I would have no one to accompany me to Chinese restaurants any more. Would I dare go alone? I went upstairs to dress for Saturday duty at Ciao. I had thought I was so adult with my solitary sex and my collection of inherited pornography and my reading of Freud, but up against a sister swooning over a Vespa-rider and a mother being devoured by the bedroom eyes of an Italian waiter, I was at a loss.

I reached Ciao by twelve, eager to study this Vito. I took my seat behind the cash register as my father, menus in hand, welcomed the customers. He had begun to recognise the regulars and was accepted by them as charming and unassuming, and probably Italian. Ha! I thought. Little did they know.

Vito was hard to study as he was usually in a blur of movement. He was a Roman-style waiter for whom balancing four heaped plates of ravioli or juggling four cappuccinos was a challenge, a matter of pride. When he smiled, everything flashed – his eyes, his teeth, even his glistening black hair. He was on the short side, with a bustling arrogance to make up for it and he had an aquiline nose and huge pale blue eyes, lushly fringed in black. His grooming was painfully impeccable, face and hands so scrubbed that there was a hint of self-punishment about all the red skin. His way of moving was stylised, bowing and drawing out chairs and shoving them, with a flourish, under ladies' bottoms. He nodded gravely at the most banal choices, as if complimenting the customer. He was earning the best tips.

'That one's going places,' Marie predicted, handing me a bill with a five-pound note, keeping her eyes on Vito. 'Your dad had better watch out, the way he's eyeing your mother.'

I did not like her talking in that way and gave her the change very disapprovingly, watching Vito serve four *espressos*. It was his idea to add a twist of lemon peel to the saucer, 'as they do in Roma'. Dad only agreed to it because Vito spent his own time industriously carving peel from the chef's discarded lemons. I thought, in spite of myself, that it was a most sophisticated touch, even though no one ever did anything with the peel. The idea of any romance between Vito and my mother seemed quite unimaginable: he was almost young enough to be her son.

The following Friday, it was announced that Vito would be coming home to cook Dad's favourite dish, *Sole Bonne Femme*. No stranger had ever cooked in our kitchen before. It was to be a command performance.

*

My parents appointed Marie deputy manager and Vito, clutching shopping-bags crammed with fish, bustled into our house. He shook our hands, bowed, smiled, whisked the ingredients out of his bags with a flourish, inspected our pans and deemed them adequate. He kept grinning at my mother, whom he called Mrs Conway, his buffed white teeth flashing each time he indicated she could pass before him into the kitchen or back into the dining room. Dad buried himself in the *Evening News*.

The *Sole Bonne Femme* was prepared and cooked as if Vito had invented it that very evening. It was pretty good, although not nearly as good as Vito's dramatic gestures indicated. He nearly swooned when he took his first mouthful. When Dad requested a second helping, Vito beamed with pride. I had seen him pour half a bottle of white wine into the sauce: alcohol was not good for my father's ulcer. Dad retired to bed early, thanking Vito for the meal. My mother walked him to the bus stop. Rachel and I washed up.

'She's in lo-o-ove …' Rachel sang.

'Don't be so stupid, she couldn't be,' I answered, irritated. 'No one could be in love with Vito – he's too much in love with himself.'

Rachel gave me a knowing look. 'If I were married to Dad, I'd be in love with Vito,' she sighed.

'Mum just likes being admired,' I said, drying a plate. 'Dad takes her for granted and now a younger man is showing her she's still attractive to men, that's all.'

'You don't know women.' Rachel smiled secretively. 'You don't know how many times Mum has nearly left Dad. She only stays because of us. While she was hidden away in the house, their marriage was fairly safe. Now that she's meeting new men all the time, I give their marriage six months.'

I laughed. No Willesden wife ever left her husband, particularly for a younger Italian waiter. Life was too predictable. It was considered shocking that Mum was learning to *drive*!

*

Grandma took to her bed. We were told not to visit her. She wasn't exactly ill, it was more like the 'mourning period' of last year, when Jack had been airborne. He wasn't airborne this time, but to Grandma his journey was equally dangerous. In both cases, she faced losing her son.

She stayed in her bedroom for ten days. During that period, she underwent the most remarkable transformation. She had retired to bed in a tragic mood, convinced that a Gentile daughter-in-law was the worst thing that could befall her. She emerged – after a wave of her own magic wand – convinced it was the best. The word *shiksa* was banished from her vocabulary (and thus from everyone else's), to be replaced by 'film star'. It was no longer 'My son's marrying a *shiksa*' but 'My son's marrying a film star'. In this way, she transformed overnight the image of 'marrying out' from something sordid into something glamorous. She really ought to have been in public relations.

'She's so beautiful,' Grandma told her cronies, who came flocking back to the flat to welcome Grandma on the day of her comeback. 'Blonde, pretty ... *slim*!' She held up a forefinger, staring at them triumphantly, knowing that most of their Jewish daughters-in-law were plump or even fat. No one dared point out that a plump Jewish daughter-in-law was worth ten slim 'film stars'.

'Pity 'er father won't be allowed under the *chuppah*,'

she said sadly. 'But you can't go against the rules of the religion.'

The cronies clucked sympathetically, exchanging glances. They knew very well that one nod from Grandma to the rabbi would allow anyone she wanted under the *chuppah*, but they understood she had to draw the line somewhere. They were in awe of Grandma; she was their ideal of what a strong, loving wife and mother should be.

'What *mazel* for 'er, eh?' Grandma prodded, dabbing her eyes. 'Gettin' a 'usband like my Jack!'

On that, the cronies and the Brass Ladies could sincerely agree.

19

The Wedding

Weddings were not supposed to be like Jack's wedding to Christine. In our family, *simchas* had always been exciting, lavish occasions with flowers and orchestras and glamorous ball-gowns. There was nothing lavish about the Kilburn Liberal Reform Synagogue on a damp November Sunday. The aroma of a *simcha*, that heady mixture of smoked salmon canapés, perfume and cigars, was absent. No flowers decorated the bleak hall. There were no ball-gowns because there was to be no ball, no giggling bridesmaids, no celebratory champagne feeling, no champagne. We had been instructed not to dress up. Lawrence and I wore our school blazers with grey flannels, white shirts and ties. The men were in dark suits, the women in cocktail dresses. Only the Brass Ladies added a touch of glamour with their gold jewellery and bright satin dresses in emerald or purple peeking from beneath mink stoles.

We milled around outside the synagogue, our feet crunching on the gravel, awaiting the bride. Even that would be, we knew, an anticlimax, Grandma having made the proclamation that Christine couldn't wear white. The happy couple, dazed by their good luck, had given in on everything. Christine was not going to appear in a fairytale crinoline and I don't think she cared that much. All she wanted was Jack.

As we waited, I stared at the guests. Grandma had only invited people she couldn't *not* invite. These included the Whitechapel branch of the family and the Denham cousins whom we rarely saw. There were a few weird great-aunts, who were said to be mad, their weirder husbands and their even weirder daughters. Each had some physical deformity: crossed eyes or squints, or (if female) beards. Although we giggled about these distant cousins, we were also slightly afraid of them. They never mingled or spoke, but hovered on the outskirts of family functions, squinting at us. Lawrence and I were obliged to greet them and kiss the women, which we did early on, to get it over with.

Watching the crowd grow, my mother sighed. 'I've been to funerals that were more fun than this,' she told Joyce.

Joyce shivered, snuggling into her coat. 'It just doesn't *feel* like a wedding!' she complained.

A humble car drove up with Christine and her father in the back, Hilda driving. No white ribbon decorated the vehicle. We watched it come to a standstill. Hilda got out first. She had made a great effort with her flower-bedecked hat and matching floral-print coat and dress. It was more Buckingham Palace garden party than Kilburn Liberal Synagogue, but at least it was colourful. From the grim set of her lipsticked mouth, it was clear that this was an ordeal she was steeling herself to get through. As Christine alighted there was a murmur from the onlookers, many of whom were seeing her for the first time.

'Like a film star,' one of Grandma's cronies gasped, obediently using Grandma's expression.

'So *slim*,' a Brass Lady marvelled.

Christine's dove-grey velvet dress neither disguised nor emphasised the bulge of her stomach. Softly gathered just above the waist, the skirt dipped to 'ballerina length', showing off small grey pumps. The only touch of colour was a small bouquet of pink roses and her subtly made-up pale face. Her blonde hair was piled up on her head and tiny silk roses pinned in it. Her expression grave, she sailed past, almost regally aloof.

Her father was tall and slim. He looked to be in his late sixties and his grey hair and subdued manner made him seem fragile and tired. He moved like an old man, and Hilda hovered near, with a hand on his arm. As the bride disappeared into the building, the guests should have taken their seats, but there seemed to be an unspoken agreement to wait around for the real star of the afternoon. Everyone wanted to see what Grandma would look like, how she would carry this off, what her expression or way of dressing would signify. Would she be crying, smiling, dressed-up, dressed-down, what? We did not have long to wait.

The silver Jaguar drew up, with Jack at the wheel. Everyone pressed forward. Mary was first out, opening the back door to haul out her mistress. There was a flash of white bloomers as Grandma staggered to her feet, puffing herself up with – if not pride – then importance. She had dressed down, in a plain black dress and fur coat, but had made up for it with an astonishing display of jewellery, her best rubies, fished out of the Egg & I safe for the occasion. She must have wanted to intimidate Hilda, because everyone else had seen them before. The great aunts, who were wearing tiny diamond pins ('Chips,' my mother sniffed), squinted hard and critically at Grandma.

Grandma drew herself up to her full height and the rubies flashed in the dull Kilburn light. Mary fussed around and Grandma made some annoyed, flicking gestures for her to stop. In truth she presented a frightening image, her make-up whiter than usual, as if she had applied several coats of flour to her face, a slash of crimson on her lips. She sported a downturned grimace, the mask of Tragedy. Some orange curls peeked out from beneath a new black satin cloche, which was rammed, as usual, down to her eyes.

Grandpa was neat but dazed and resigned, in a dark suit. His mouth was set in a straight, determined line.

The crowd parted for them to walk through.

'God, this is grim,' Joyce groaned, as we followed them into the building and caught a distinct smell of stale school dinners.

Why was she so disapproving, I wondered. Did she feel that Jack marrying out of the religion might be setting a dangerous new precedent? If one brother disobeyed his mother, what was to stop the other brother from following suit? Could she be thinking that? My mind buzzed with all the undercurrents of this unique occasion.

My mother (we were experiencing the rare novelty of mixing with women in a synagogue, as the Liberal was desegregated) had a distant, dreamy expression. Could she possibly be in love with Vito, as Rachel insisted? If I pretended I was following the story of a film, I could just consider this, although it raised all kinds of strange, conflicting emotions. I could be proud of her for considering leaving Dad, but not for choosing someone as ghastly as Vito. The dreary synagogue was totally different from the rich red velvet and gilt trappings of our Willesden *shul*, the *chuppah* as utilitarian and plain as a Meccano set, with its indented, grey metal top. I tried to work out whether Jack's marriage somehow granted my mother permission for romance with an Italian waiter. It was a little beyond me, and our arrival at the door of the *shul* ended my puzzled thoughts. We took our places in a front row, me, my brother, my sister and our parents settled on the wood bench prepared for an hour of boredom. Hilda entered the row behind and I caught her eye.

'Christine looks beautiful,' I told her. She gave me a smile and I thought she glanced wistfully at my parents' backs. 'Mum? Dad?' I alerted them. 'This is Hilda.'

'Of course. Hello, Hilda.' Mum twisted round to greet her with a smile, holding out her hand. She seemed slightly embarrassed. No one was introducing anyone to anyone, so I prodded my father.

'Dad?' I leaned to tap his shoulder. 'It's Hilda.' They smiled and shook hands, but the atmosphere was constrained; they did not compliment her or say the things I had expected them to say.

'I'm only perching here for a moment,' Hilda chattered. 'People always cry at weddings, don't they? I thought I'd be different, but here I am, crying before the wedding.' She wiped a tear from her eyes and dabbed at imaginary mascara marks. 'They're such a tiny family, you see. They only realised today how small they are: a father, a daughter, a few cousins, and me. And *I'm* not even related!'

'Howard tells me you've been like a mother to her,' my mother said kindly, but this brought on a fresh torrent of tears. My parents discreetly turned back to face the *chuppah*.

A young rabbi wrapped a glass in a napkin and placed it on the floor to be crushed underfoot by the groom at the ceremony's climax. No one had laid eyes on this rabbi before today. Unlike Orthodox families, we rarely got the same rabbi twice at ceremonies, and this unfamiliar synagogue with its strange liberal laws added another odd layer to the mood. I tried to analyse it. We didn't feel like a group of people celebrating a marriage, more like a group waiting to see if it would really happen, if Grandma was going to allow it to happen. She could pretend to be happy and rave all she liked about Christine's beauty and slimness, but the facts – the flowerless, bridesmaidless *shul* – spoke for themselves.

'Is she really going to allow it to go ahead?' I whispered to Rachel. 'Or will she pull some magic trick out of her hat?'

'Like a rabbit? To stop the wedding?' Rachel giggled. 'How?'

''Ilda Williams.' Grandma's voice behind us broke my reverie. 'You're too near.'

I swivelled round to see Grandma standing in the aisle, wagging her finger at Hilda.

'You're too near the *chuppah*,' she said.

Hilda swallowed. I could hear how dry her throat was. 'But I'm not under the *chuppah*, Mrs G,' she said pleasantly, though her teeth were slightly clenched.

'I want you as far away from it as possible,' Grandma said, waving her arm. 'The rabbi won't like it.'

'No, Mum,' my mother spoke up. 'Just as long as she's not under it.'

Grandma gave her a withering stare. A squinting great-aunt behind Hilda craned her neck to try to see her. Hilda cleared her throat. Her bright little black eyes narrowed behind their powerful lenses. She took a deep, patient breath.

'Where do you want me to sit, Mrs G?' she asked.

Grandma pointed to the last row of seats. 'The back,' she said.

Hilda gasped. I twisted around, staring at her face, willing her to stand up to Grandma. I felt I could read Hilda's mind, see exactly what she was thinking. I saw the almost irresistible temptation to tell Grandma to go to hell, but I also saw her attempt to control it, her telling herself, 'We're so near, so near to victory. Don't throw it all away just for a few more minutes' worth of patience.' She got to her feet. The flowered hat gave her a slight advantage in height and she made the most of it as she moved down the row towards Grandma. When she reached the aisle, Grandma barely moved one millimetre to the side.

Hilda faced her for a moment, then said, 'I think I'll go help Christine,' and sailed down the aisle. I could see Grandpa near the rabbi, looking on, a tic of nervous tension working in his forehead.

One of Grandma's Brass Ladies bustled up and embraced Grandma.

'*Mazeltov*, Mrs G,' she gushed. 'My, you look fabulous!'

'Don't *mazeltov* me yet,' Grandma growled. 'They're not married yet. I could drop dead in the next five minutes.'

The Brass Lady screamed and pretended to spit. 'Don't even say that, Mrs G!' she cried. 'You'll outlive us all.'

'Yeah,' Grandma said grimly, moving towards the *chuppah*. 'Outlive you all.'

The organist began to play a discreet dirge. Everyone fell silent. Jack, Grandpa and Grandma, directed by the rabbi, took their places. The rabbi nodded to someone in the doorway, glancing up at the organist in the balcony. The organist stopped what he was playing and began 'The Wedding March'.

One step at a time, Christine advanced down the aisle on her father's arm. Neither smiled, they both looked as if they were about to burst into tears. I could see so clearly that they were both thinking, 'If only my mother/my wife were here ...'. I watched, fascinated, as they took their slow, measured steps. Uncle Jack turned to watch, his black eyes anxious.

Christine passed us, her profile with its tiny nose and

gently parted lips like a Victorian cameo. Mr Higgins delivered his daughter to the assigned spot beside Jack, then
made to walk to the back of the synagogue. Hilda had
crept back to her seat behind us, no doubt figuring that
Grandma's back being towards her, she would be left in
peace. But Grandpa's hand detained Christine's father,
and his other hand beckoned Hilda to join them.

There was a flicker of annoyance on the young rabbi's
face at these two unexpected additions to the family line-
up, then a shrug. The sooner this crazy bunch gets out of
this synagogue, the better, I could see him thinking. Rachel
dug me in the ribs. My heart leapt.

Grandma, her mouth twisted to one side like a ventril-
oquist's, snarled, 'They can't stand 'ere.'

'They're standing here. I want them here,' Grandpa
said. Rachel dug me in the ribs again, so hard that I gasped.

'Dad!' Jack burst out. Christine's eyes widened.

'They can't stand under the *chuppah*! They're not
Jewish.' Grandma's eyes flashed. 'The father can go in the
first row, but 'Ilda Williams must sit at the back. I *told* 'er!'

'And I'm telling them to stand here,' Grandpa said.

Hilda stared straight ahead, the other side of Grandpa.
Mr Higgins looked completely nonplussed. The organ
continued to play. Some guests fidgeted. The moment
stretched itself out. Grandma faced Grandpa.

'There'll be murders if she doesn't sit at the back,' she
said warningly. 'We must do as the rabbi says. Isn't that
right, rabbi?'

'Well, I … er …' the rabbi looked as if he would expire
if Grandma challenged him.

Grandpa shifted to face Grandma. Thirty-eight years of
marriage flashed between their eyes. I had never seen
Grandpa look so stern or the vein in his temple throb so
much. Was this Grandma's plan? To bring on some kind of
funny turn, scuppering everything?

'Christine's lost her mother,' Grandpa explained
quietly. 'I think her father should stand here with us, as a
mark of respect. And Hilda too.'

'Oh, Mr G,' Hilda sobbed quietly.

'I'll walk out, Max,' Grandma said.

'You want them to get married without you?' Grandpa suggested.

Grandma glared at him.

'Mary,' she summoned, and Mary popped up from the front row. 'I feel faint,' Grandma said, swaying. Mary waved the smelling salts under her mistress's nose and Grandma clutched a support of the *chuppah*, making it rock.

'Don't faint, you'll miss the wedding,' Grandpa advised. 'You wouldn't want to miss your son's wedding, would you?'

We waited, breathless. Amazingly, Grandma gave him one last black look, then a massive shrug before falling silent. She would get her revenge somehow, and it would be terrible, but it was for exactly this reason that everyone felt that Grandpa had been so brave. He had won this round.

The ceremony proceeded. 'The Wedding March' ceased (it had played about eight times) and the service began. It was conducted in English and was mercifully brief. Christine's father stared straight ahead, a slight smile on his lips, and Hilda was so proud and dignified that I wanted to cheer. When Jack stamped on the napkin-covered glass, everyone cried '*Mazeltov*!' They were married!

The couple signed the register. When they turned, Christine was smiling. Her eyes had lost their grave sadness and she seemed to have a new assurance, now that she knew she was Mrs Jack G and no one could take it away from her. Jack beamed as people surged out of their seats and mobbed the couple as they attempted to make their way down the aisle. Everyone kissed everyone. Hilda looked relieved and smiled. Grandpa's face had relaxed.

I grabbed him to say, 'That was a wonderful thing you did, including Christine's father and Hilda –'

'You think so?' He eyed me sharply. 'I wish my wife agreed.'

I craned to see Grandma's face as she walked from the

chuppah. Tears had left tracks in her thick white make-up and her eyes, bloodshot from crying, glowed with a mad red light. As her sisters, cronies, cousins and friends rushed to kiss and congratulate her, she forced a sickly smile and pretended to allow them to jolly her out of her beaten mood. But 'Grandma' and 'beaten mood' was a contradiction in terms: she would find a way to make giving in to her husband's wishes appear noble and praiseworthy, and at the same time she would plan her revenge. There was time to get her revenge – a whole lifetime. This gave her something to look forward to and her mouth set in a determined smile.

'There'll be murders tonight – when everyone's gone,' my mother predicted.

Later, I heard her take Frankie to one side and murmur gleefully, 'Well? They did it.' And they exchanged mischievous looks as if they were in cahoots and up to something. Puzzled, I wondered what that could be.

Everyone went back to my grandparents' flat for a festive high tea. Platters of fishcakes, chicken legs and bagels draped in smoked salmon were handed around and guests dipped into bowls of pickled cucumbers, olives, nuts and crisps. Trays of teacups awaited a large urn to spout its boiling brew, but some people asked for, or needed, a real drink. The glittering best room was thrown open, its white sheeting and plastic covers banished for the afternoon. People poured into the flat and fur coats piled up on Grandma's bed to form a hairy mountain. Men lit cigars then removed them from their mouths to cram in a bagel. For a few hours, it smelled like a wedding. The feast continued into the evening, Grandma playing the role of gracious, if slightly subdued, hostess, Christine that of demure bride, and Jack the proud husband. Hilda made sure Christine's father was seated comfortably in a quiet corner and ferried drinks and snacks to him. The poor man looked quite dazed by it all. I watched Jack and Christine underplaying their happiness, as if it might still be suddenly snatched away from them. The weird cousins and great-aunts stood in a corner, eating and squinting angrily at everyone, as if storing up evidence. 'Every family has some,' my mother sighed, glancing at them and smiling. The thousands of mirrored squares covering the cocktail cabinets and side-tables reflected the beaming, eating, smoking faces in their surfaces.

Grandpa lit up a Havana he had been saving for a special occasion and its fragrant aroma filled the air. Then an unexpected cabaret: we crowded into the kitchen to watch, breathless and shocked, as Joyce breast-fed her baby, which had been brought to the flat by its nanny. Unbuttoning her blouse to reveal a swollen breast, Joyce calmly stuck her nipple into her son's open mouth. Nothing like this had ever been seen before in our prudish family. I stored the sight as 'ammunition' for my sexual fantasies. I would substitute Marilyn Monroe's face for Joyce's.

By seven o'clock the platters had been stripped down to their last fishcake, salmon-bagel-half, and chicken leg. The men were sitting down to a hand of poker and the newly-weds, after a quick trip to their flat, returned to say their goodbyes, *en route* to a secret honeymoon destination that everyone knew was in the South of France. We waved them off and everyone began to leave. The wedding of Jack to Christine had been absorbed into our family life.

My parents drove us home, changed, and returned to Soho to boost the evening's takings. We were left to the anticlimax of a dull evening at home; except that it wasn't a dull evening, it was the night I became a man.

20

Death of a Father Figure

I remember that evening down to the tiniest detail. It began with my brother emptying pocketfuls of cashew nuts onto his bed.

'Thief,' I accused him. He shrugged and switched on the television we now had in our room, sitting before it and eating nuts. I glanced at the back of his head: did my sketchbook really need its umpteenth study? I decided not.

Rachel popped her head round the door. 'I'm going to see Peggy Parisiac,' she told us. She always called her best friend by her full name. I knew she wanted to recount the day's events. I got involved in a novel. Somerset Maugham. Old-fashioned but reliable.

The telephone rang just after nine.

'Howard? Hilda here, dear. Is your mum around? Or your dad?' She sounded strained, nervous.

'No, they're at the restaurant. Is anything wrong?'

'It's your grandfather,' she said, and I thought I heard a slight sob. 'One of his funny turns, I think.'

'Is he in your flat?' I asked, frowning.

'Yes, and I want to get him home, but I need someone to lend a hand. Howard, do you think *you* could just jump into a taxi?'

'I'm not sure I have enough money,' I said, hesitating.

'I'll pay this end. Just tell the driver to wait while you ring my bell. I wouldn't ask, but he's breathing rather heavily. I can hardly ask your grandmother –'

'Why not?' I blurted out.

Hilda gave an embarrassed gurgle. 'Well … you see … the problem is, he's in my bed.'

*

Willesden High Street on a Sunday night is not exactly the crossroads of the world. I had to wait a long time before spotting a taxi cruising down the hill from Willesden Green Station. My heart beat fast in the taxi, a mixture of anxiety at the meter ticking up a sum I did not possess and apprehension at how I was going to find the strength to drag Grandpa out of Hilda's bed, down the street and into his own bed. I pictured Hilda and me draping his arms around our shoulders, sharing his weight and moving forward one step at a time. But how were we going to get him down her steep flight of stairs?

Hilda looked pale when she came down to pay the fare. She had changed into a navy dress and was clutching a cardigan over her shoulders. She kissed me and led the way up.

'He's in there,' she said, opening her bedroom door. 'He needed a lie down. You know what he's like with his naps. *Schluffs*, he calls them.' She laughed, then lowered her voice. 'Says they restore him. But then I couldn't budge him.'

I went in with the greatest foreboding. Grandpa was on his back, his eyes closed, his pink body mostly under the bedclothes. I could see his white vest and noticed his navy suit, the suit he had worn at the wedding, hanging over the back of a flowery, slip-covered chair. His shiny black shoes were neatly lined up to the side. I walked towards him with the intention of gently shaking him awake, but halfway there I stopped, an icy rush of sweat drenching my body. Instinctively I wanted to turn and run away. I did turn, but Hilda grabbed my arm, stopping me.

'What?' she cried in such a strange voice that I knew she had known – she had needed someone to confirm it.

'He's dead,' I whispered. I had never seen a dead person before but I knew. The room was too silent, too still. The special atmosphere of a room with a dead body in it. A corpse.

'No!' Hilda cried. 'No, he can't be. He was breathing

quite normally when I phoned you – almost snoring. Oh!'
Her hand shot to her mouth, her eyes wide. 'Oh, don't tell
me it was the death rattle.'

I could hardly look at the bed. It was as if I had loved
him too much alive to accept looking at him dead. The
horror seemed overwhelming. Still holding each other,
Hilda and I gingerly approached the bed. Grandpa seemed
to be asleep. And perfectly content. His mouth was set in a
pleasant straight line, his eyes closed.

'Oh God! What will I do?' Hilda wailed. She had lost all
her usual coolness and her eyes darted around the room.
'Your grandmother!' She turned to me. 'We were going to
get him home, weren't we? I thought together we could –
and now he's dead. Oh, poor man – what a day to die on –
oh, how I'll miss you, Max.' She knelt down by the bed and
took Grandpa's hand.

I turned away, a succession of absurd plans flashing
through my mind – stuffing Grandpa into a suitcase and
dragging it home; dressing him and pretending he had
collapsed in the street. I knew I would be unable to put
either of these crazy schemes into operation. I would be
unable even to touch him.

'He was the best person I knew in this world.' Hilda's
voice rose high on the last word and her mouth twisted to
one side. She put Grandpa's hand carefully on his chest.
For a moment, I feared she might press his two hands
together in a praying gesture. Sitting down heavily on
Grandpa's suit, she stared at me.

'I think I'm going to be sick,' I warned.

She rushed me into the bathroom and I leaned over the
sink as she slammed the door behind her. The nausea
passed. I ran the water cold and splashed my face, trying to
make my mind accept what had happened and think what
we should do, who we should call. I tried to understand
that I would never talk to Grandpa again – I had so many
more questions for him, I didn't even know where he had
been born. I patted my face with Hilda's pink towel and
stared into my eyes in the mirror, not crying. After all the
many Saturday afternoons with Grandpa snoring gently

beside me in the flea-pit cinema, the milk-shakes later, the glass animals for my collection, surely I could squeeze out a few tears by thinking that we were never going to do any of that together again. The way he had sung '*Ridi, Pagliaccio …*' under his breath: 'Laugh, clown' – was that how he saw himself? Had he really sung in the Paris Opera? I had never dared to ask him in case it forced him to admit he hadn't. I shocked myself by being unable to cry.

Hilda was rummaging through the kitchen drawers when I emerged. I stood in the doorway, watching her.

'I'm looking for a candle,' she explained. 'Christine told me when a Jewish person dies, you must light a candle: it comforts the departing soul.'

I glanced at the door of her bedroom as if I expected to see Grandpa's soul float out.

'You drape mirrors with sheets so you don't see your own reflection,' I added mechanically.

Hilda held up a candle. 'I'll leave that to your grandmother,' she said, lighting it and dripping wax into a saucer. 'She's the Jewish one.'

Shielding the flame, she carried the candle into her bedroom, setting it beside the bed, flicking off the main light. I thought Grandpa's face moved, but it was the flickering shadows the candle made. I stayed by the door, furious at myself for not kissing his forehead, at least. But I couldn't.

'Call his son!' Hilda cried suddenly. 'Phone your Uncle Frankie. *He'll* know what to do. We've got to get your Grandpa home.' I dialled Joyce's number on the black telephone. Uncle Frankie answered, brusque and businesslike.

'Uncle Frankie? It's Howard here.'

'Yes?'

'I'm sorry to disturb you, but … it's Grandpa … he's …'

'What's wrong?'

'I'm at Hilda's flat. I … Grandpa's here. He's …'

'Let me speak to him.'

'We –' I faltered. 'We think he's dead.'

'Oh my God! Does your grandmother know?'

'Not yet. I –'

'I'll be right over.' He hung up.

I stared at Hilda. 'He's coming,' I told her.

She got up from where she was sitting, at the foot of her bed, gazing at Grandpa, and came towards me, closing the bedroom door behind her.

'You know what we need?' she said. 'Hot, sweet tea. Like they give people in shock. We're both in shock, you know.'

I followed her into the kitchen and watched her put water on to boil and clatter teacups into saucers.

'Someone had better tell your grandmother,' she began. 'I can't. Not after all that's happened today. Your grandfather arrived here in such a state. They'd had a terrible row. I can't very well go over there and say "Mrs G, your husband's just died in my bed." I'm sorry, Howard, but I just *can't*.' She buried her face in her hands. 'She jawed him to death, she did,' she cried in a muffled voice. 'I blame her, I really do.'

I stood near her, touching her shoulder. This was my moment to become a man, over two years after my barmitzvah. If I could find the courage to tell Grandma that her husband was dead, I would surely have earned my manhood. For I blamed Grandma too. I could imagine their last row and the fury she had unleashed onto Grandpa the moment their guests had left. Having played gracious hostess for three hours would only have encouraged her rage to simmer, until it had exploded. He had made her look stupid before all her family, friends and cronies and she would not forgive that lightly. She had forced him out of his warm flat into the cold street to seek Hilda's shelter. Perhaps he had left in silent pride, not even saying goodbye. I shook my head. I could think only of the candlelight flickering across his pale face and his two shiny shoes lined up so neatly by the chair. What did any of it matter now?

I pulled on my coat. Hilda uncovered her face and looked at me with pathetically grateful eyes.

'*I'll* tell her,' I said. 'I'll probably come back with her.'

What seemed simple and logical in Hilda's flat seemed less so in the reality of the dark street. When I reached Grandma's entrance, my new-found courage deserted me and I continued on, past her door, telling myself I would take a walk around the block. Perhaps Uncle Frankie would miraculously arrive before me and he could be the one to break the news. No! I quickened my steps. I was going to tell her.

Where was Grandpa's soul right then? Was it being comforted by a lit candle, hovering over the bed watching Hilda, or with me now in the dark street? Had he seen that I couldn't cry and was too scared to touch him? I began to realise what I had lost. All the years of reading Freud suddenly sank in. I had made Grandpa my father figure because my own father had not been up to the job. My mother had always maintained that my father loved me, but I had never believed it. Grandpa had loved me, had treated me as an equal. And now I no longer had even a father substitute.

I reached the entrance again and this time I went up. I tried to visualise Grandma's reaction. She would have to perform all the rituals we had learned in Hebrew classes: draping the mirrors, making sure my uncles didn't shave for a week, hiring low chairs so that mourners could sit very close to the floor in the week of sitting *shiva*. Friends would bring her food like eggs or bread. For the entire week, we would be Jewish again, as we were at births, marriages and barmitzvahs. And funerals.

Grandma opened the door fresh from a marathon washing-up session. The best room was still open and blazingly lit, to receive the armfuls of dishes and trays of glasses she stored there. She had removed the rubies and the black dress and was in her overalls over her white satin slip. She looked at me sharply, not at all welcoming, knowing that I would not appear out of nowhere, late on a Sunday evening, unless it was for something serious. She did not attempt a smile.

'What's wrong?' she snapped.

'Grandpa,' I tried to say, but I could not form the word.

'Uncle Frankie,' I blurted out instead. 'He's coming. He's got something to tell you – he'll be here in a few minutes.'

'No!' she yelled. It was as if she knew. She gripped both my arms painfully tight. '*You* tell me!' She said it almost like a dare, her eyes popping with the glare she gave me.

'Grandpa –' I began, then fell speechless. I should have rehearsed what I intended to say. I reached out for her but she drew away and puffed herself up, her senses quivering as she awaited my words.

'Grandpa's dead,' I said.

She glared at me. She looked quite affronted. 'What are you talkin' about, *dead*?' she cried. She pretended to spit a couple of times. '*Ptui! Ptui!*' The Jewish dry spit to ward off evil news. ''E's probably 'avin' one of 'is funny turns, that's all. 'Ave you tried shoutin' in 'is ear? Shakin' 'im? Screamin' an' yellin'? Where is 'e? *I'll* bring 'im back.'

'He's at Hilda's, Grandma,' I told her.

''Ilda's?' she screamed. ''Ilda Williams? What's 'e doin' *there*? 'E said 'e was goin' for a walk. 'Asn't that woman caused enough trouble for one day – standin' under the *chuppah* when she 'ad no right?'

She looked around for her coat, kicking off her slippers. She hurried into her bedroom, shucking her overalls, slipping into her black dress and presenting the back to me to zip up.

'I'll go round there – where does she live? I'll scream at 'im to come back. I always get 'im back, you'll see.'

She rammed her hat on her head and slipped on her shoes. Half of this was acting, I knew. She couldn't have thought Grandpa would walk up and down the Edgware Road for hours on a Sunday night. She didn't sound surprised to learn that Hilda lived so close.

'I'll scream at 'im, I'll get 'im back,' she said to herself as she locked the door.

I followed her down the stairs, watching her wrap her fur coat tightly around her. She sounded so sure of herself that I wanted to believe her. Perhaps she *would* make everything all right. I had seen her raise Grandpa from the nearly-dead once before, why not again tonight? We left the building and I tried to ignore my certainty that he was dead and nothing in the world could change that.

Grandma walked so quickly that I could barely keep up, her head down against the cold wind that blew through the narrow street between the high red-brick mansion flats, muttering to herself.

'That man would sleep all day and all night if you let 'im,' I heard.

Hilda was standing by the open door on the street and Grandma just sailed through and up the stairs, as if she had visited many times. The protocol of such occasions had to be invented as we went along. Hilda and I followed.

When she got inside the small entrance hall, Grandma hesitated for just a moment, then headed for the bedroom. She blew out the candle as she reached the bed.

''Ow *dare* you light a candle!' She turned to scream at Hilda. ''E's not dead *yet*. Not by a long way.'

Hilda began to say something, then checked herself, darting me a helpless glance. Grandma climbed clumsily up on to the bed and took Grandpa's shoulders in her hands. She filled her lungs with air and began to scream '*Max*?' as I ducked out of the room, Hilda following.

*

We waited just outside the room, shocked, rigid, frozen, yet still slightly hopeful, as if Grandma could still work some magic, as if her pleadings and entreaties really would prove effective. Her cries were angry, then pitiful, disbelieving, then almost resigned. I told myself not to look, but after a while I glanced in and wished I hadn't. Grandpa's head was lolling back, his mouth slackly open, limp as a rag doll as his wife shook him like some large blackbird with a victim in its claws. Finally, Hilda ran in.

'That's enough now, Mrs G,' she said, gently placing her hands over Grandma's. 'Let him rest. He deserves it.'

I waited for Grandma to resist Hilda, perhaps hit her, but she loosened her grip and the determined expression left her face. With a resigned slump of her shoulders, she allowed Grandpa's body to fall gently back onto the pillows.

'G'bye, Max,' she called in a wavery high voice I had never heard before. 'G'bye, darlin'!'

She leaned to kiss him more tenderly than I had ever seen her kiss him alive. Cooing and murmuring over him, she planted little kisses over his face. I began to cry. Finally, Grandma clambered off the bed, stood up straight, turned to Hilda and spat full in her face.

''Appy now?' she screamed. '*Now* you can light the candle!'

Hilda was too surprised even to wipe away the spittle.

'What did you do to 'im?' Grandma cried. 'It wasn't enough you were 'is fancy woman all these years, 'e 'ad to die in your bed too?'

'Mrs G, you're upset and you're going to say things you –' Hilda began. I sprang to her side, taking her arm.

'Don't Mrs G me!' Grandma held up a hand. 'You 'ave no right to speak to me. I want 'im back in 'is own bed tonight. You 'ear me? My son will be 'ere, 'e'll arrange it. My sons look after me. They *respect* their parents. They'll see their father dies in 'is own bed. Come on, 'Oward.' She grabbed me and pulled me towards her. 'We'll find 'is suit – the suit 'e wants to be buried in.'

I looked at Hilda. Her eyes were beaten and guilty. My heart went out to her but my arm was in Grandma's firm grip. She jerked me around to follow her out. 'I'm sorry, Hilda,' I said.

'No need to be sorry for 'er,' Grandma cried, pulling me to the stairs. 'She got what she wanted.'

I closed the door gently, catching a glimpse of Hilda walking back to her bedroom. I knew she would sit with Grandpa until someone came.

*

Walking along the street to Grandma's flat, I had the impression that I was being borne aloft by her speed and strength, my feet barely touching the ground. A burly figure awaited us outside her entrance and I recognised him as Uncle Frankie. For once he wasn't smiling.

'Ma,' he yelled, when he saw us. He ran up to us.

'She knows,' I told him.

He held out his arms to her, but she only gave him a hurried peck. 'You go up there and bring your father 'ome,' she instructed. 'You'll need two men – 'e's 'eavy. I want 'im in 'is own bed tonight, you 'ear me?'

Frankie nodded and walked off towards Hilda's. Another family member who knew where she lived, I thought. We went upstairs to the flat. In the kitchen, Grandma rummaged through the sideboard drawers without removing her coat. When she found a bunch of keys, she grabbed me again and pulled me down the passage to the front door.

'We'll go down to the cellar,' she announced. 'That's where 'is wedding suit is.'

I knew Jews were usually buried in a white shroud but this wasn't the time to argue the finer points of Jewish burial practices with her.

'He was *wearing* a nice suit,' I said. 'The suit he wore this afternoon.'

She stopped on the staircase to glare at me. 'You think I want 'im buried in the suit 'e wore to visit 'is fancy woman?' she cried. 'No – they want to be buried in the suits they married in. That's 'ow they did things in the village 'e came from – the little village in Poland.' She beckoned me to keep walking downstairs with her. 'Bloody bunch of peasants, that lot,' she muttered under her breath.

'Shouldn't I call my mother?' I asked.

'All in good time,' Grandma said. 'I don't want everyone goin' up *there*.' She indicated Hilda's flat with a jerk of her head. 'And don't you dare say a word about any of this to anyone, you 'ear me? You 'ear me, 'Oward? There'll be murders if you breathe one word – even to your mother.'

We reached the basement. In the gap between the building and the street, a row of what had been coal bunkers were fitted with doors and padlocks for tenants to use as store-rooms. Grandma fiddled with the keys until she found the right one and then opened the door and flicked on a light. A dull bulb, swagged in cobwebs, swung dimly to show suitcases, boxes and bags piled up high. There was a rusty table and a folding iron chair set up. Grandma attacked the suitcases with manic energy, ripping them open, scattering the contents and tossing them aside. She finally found the small trunk she wanted and held up a black suit. It looked far too small for Grandpa.

''E married in *this*,' she said.

She went on rummaging until she came upon a creased tissue package. She sat on the folding chair, the package spread out on her lap, murmuring and cooing to it as if to a baby.

'I married in white,' she told me, holding up the faded dress. 'I was pure.' She stared at me in a funny way, shaking her head. 'More fool me, eh? Women *are* fools!'

'Why?' I asked.

'To put up with what *we* put up with?' she said, her eyes wide. She fell silent, playing with the dress, smoothing out its creases. Suddenly, she seemed peaceful, ready to confide.

'Did Grandpa really sing in the Paris Opera?' I asked.

'What are you talkin' about? Paris Opera!' she spluttered. ''E earned a few pennies in the claque, that's all. Clapping the singers. 'E weren't no opera singer!'

She was so dismissive of him that I began to hate her, but then I noticed the tears running silently down her cheeks.

She stared at me through the tears, and suddenly asked, ''Ow will I ever 'old my 'ead up around 'ere again? My life's over. I'll be all alone. No one will want to know me.' She looked utterly miserable. I moved near her and touched her shoulder.

'I'm so sorry, Grandma,' I began.

'Don't you Grandma me,' she growled. 'I'm not your Grandma.'

My hand flew away from her as if she had scalded me. 'What do you mean?' I frowned, wondering if she had lost her reason. 'Of *course* you're my grandmother.'

'All this pretending has been no good for my nerves,' she muttered, throwing the dress to one side and rummaging in the suitcase. 'No good at all.' She found a handful of sepia photographs, printed on stiff photographer's cards. 'There!' She held them out. 'Your grandfather's wedding day. Does the bride look like *me*?'

I tried to see in the dim light of the cobwebby bulb. Even with the passage of time and the faded quality of the photograph, it was clear that the bride was very pretty and had a small, straight nose, bright brown eyes and a full smiling mouth.

'She looks more like my mother!' I said.

Grandma nodded. '*She* was your real Grandma, not me,' she said. My body felt chilled, then hot. 'My lovely sister Cissie. She was the one 'e really loved. She'd just 'ad your mother, died a few days later. Lost too much blood. She was beautiful, like your mother. Me – the men liked me all right but I wasn't no beauty. In them days they sometimes married the sister. 'E didn't love me, 'e just needed a mother to bring up 'is daughter. Then we 'ad the two boys and we managed to rub along. They said "love can grow". Well, it didn't grow for *'im!*'

She looked up at me and her eyes seemed so grey, so pale, that I wondered how I could ever have thought they were green. I tried to understand why she was telling me this. Was she feeling guilty for Grandpa's death, and needing to make some kind of confession? Did she realise what she was saying? As I stared at the wedding photo, something was happening to me. Some new level of reality, or maturity. I was moving towards an understanding of my family, of why Grandma had always favoured the brothers and been so critical and unloving to my mother.

'See 'ow pretty I was?' Grandma asked, placing the greyish veil over her head.

It came to just below her chin in front and hung behind, almost reaching the ground. She stood up, spreading out the veil. She twirled for me, almost girlish. The transparent veil floated around her like cigarette smoke.

''E loved the boys, 'e did, but 'e loved 'is daughter best,' she went on. 'The boys idolised 'im. Jack'll have to come back from 'is 'oneymoon! 'E'll be broken'earted. What a way to start a marriage! Idolised 'is father, my Jack did.' She began to hum softly, picking up the garments she'd thrown on the floor of the cellar, handing me the suit.

''Ere, darlin', take your grandfather's suit. We'll keep it upstairs until they bring 'im 'ome. 'Ome to 'is own bed.' She looked at me and smiled, her grey eyes suddenly crystal clear. 'Y'see, no one told me what men were like. You know what I mean. In them days, no one talked about it. You got married knowing nothin'. The wedding night, I didn't know what 'e was doin' in the bed. All I felt was the pain. Oh my God, 'ow it 'urt. And the *blood*! And the births of them two boys! You didn't get drugs in them days, you *felt* it. Lovin'? Ha! All it meant to me was more pain. After Jack was born, I told 'im: "I don't want no more! I've 'ad enough." I didn't know how they were – the men! 'Ow they 'ave to 'ave it. Make you sick. If you don't give it to them, they find someone else. 'Ow did *I* know 'e'd find some tea-lady an' set 'er up as 'is fancy woman? Not much of a choice, is it? Either you suffer that terrible pain or you know your 'usband's keepin' some tea-lady just around the corner. Every time 'e popped out, I knew 'e was goin' to visit 'er. Think I didn't know? *I* knew. Popped out every few days – that's 'ow the men are. I was jealous, ooh, yes. Every now and then I blew up and let 'im 'ave it. We didn't mention 'er but 'e knew what it was about. And now 'e dies in 'er bed, shaming me! Nice ending, eh?'

After that she sat silently as if she had made some kind of peace with herself. Had confession to a fifteen-year-old grandson seemed easier, or would she have said all that to anyone who'd been around? When we went upstairs, she was still wearing her veil and I did not dare say anything. It floated out behind her as we climbed the stairs, side by side, in a weird parody of her wedding.

21

The End of my Childhood

Grandpa had reserved a plot in an Orthodox cemetery in Kensal Green, so we were obliged to hold an Orthodox ceremony. The ceremony came with the plot. The funeral revealed the Jewish religion to me in a new, cruel light. There was nothing comforting about it. No flowers were allowed. Mourners were herded into a grim hut in the grounds at nine o'clock the following Sunday morning. A light drizzle made the air grey and cold, as if an especially dark cloud were hanging over us. I couldn't help seeing it as a grotesque repeat of the wedding, with the same people: Jack and Christine tanned from two days' sun, yet pale with grief underneath, with the squinting cousins, and the bearded great-aunts looking even gloomier than they had at the wedding, but with good cause, this time.

Our maids had often entranced us with tales of how the Irish turned funerals into wakes – jolly parties celebrating the dead person's life instead of mourning it. If only we had been Irish! There was nothing jolly about burying Grandpa, even though all his pals turned out – his barber, his barbershop cronies, his Turkish bath fellow-steamers, his poker partners, even his cigar supplier. The young female office workers who had sought his advice on their problems and adopted him as their grandfather turned up too. The service began, unremarkable until the *Kaddish* droned by a gloomy rabbi. That nasal dirge, that rasp where the voice broke at the back of the throat, summoning up Arabic or Moroccan chant, tore at me, making me promise myself I would never allow myself to hear it again. I had never despised religion so much, not least because there was nothing of Grandpa in all this. Of course I had to be present, out of respect for Grandpa: that's how religion blackmails you. Even if I didn't believe, I had to endure other people's beliefs. Although Grandpa had admitted his lack of belief to me, he had been born a Jew, he had died a Jew and he had obviously wanted to be buried as one. Why else had he paid annual fees to a synagogue he'd scarcely attended, if not for the privilege of being buried in its cemetery?

The coffin was loaded onto an old iron trolley resembling something left over from the American Civil War. This rusty thing had to be pushed by Uncle Jack and Uncle Frankie to a freshly-dug plot at the far end of the grounds, with everyone trailing behind. The trolley was so unwieldy and difficult to control and the brothers so blinded by tears, that only the rabbi's steadying hand prevented them from taking a wrong turn amongst the rows of graves. If I had planned the funeral, what wonderful arias I would have played, loudly, over the public address system. We would have had *I Pagliacci* and *The Barber of Seville* and all Grandpa's favourites.

Grandma, trembling and dazed, her face a white Kabuki mask, was supported by my mother and Joyce. I had never seen my mother looking like that. Would I look like that when she died? I knew I would – and worse – which started off a fresh torrent of my own tears. When Grandpa had been carefully lowered into the grave, we had to thrust a spade, one by one, into a mound of soil and scatter it over his coffin. It was hateful to think of Grandpa in that box and cruel, I thought, to make his relatives help bury him. But it was all part of the ritual. When my turn came, I scattered my spadeful of soil into the grave because it would have been worse to refuse and hold up the ceremony.

*

'You're in the will!' Grandma greeted me when I visited her some weeks after the funeral. She was spring-cleaning the entire flat with Mary, and I felt, perhaps unfairly, that she was trying to rid the place of all traces of Grandpa. His fat wooden hairbrush had disappeared from the bathroom and there was no aroma of cigar or cologne.

''E remembered you. 'E left you a nice sum,' Grandma went on. ''E rather fancied your bein' an artist. Always wanted to be one 'isself.' Pity he had to tell me after his death, I thought. I stopped myself from saying it. 'You'll 'ave enough to go to that art school you was tellin' me about,' Grandma nodded.

She climbed the ladder held steady by Mary who rolled her eyes heavenward at me. When Grandma reached the top, she began to scrub at a white wall, which looked perfectly clean to me.

As if reading my thoughts, Mary suddenly blurted, 'I don't know why you're doing this, Mrs G. A spotless white wall, sure!'

'What are you talking about?' Grandma cried. 'It's filthy-dirty.'

I watched them work together. I had not told anyone about Grandma not really being our grandmother. I was not sure I believed it. I felt that I had heard her confession under strange circumstances and should keep it to myself. Perhaps she had even been temporarily insane.

'Your Grandpa remembered you,' Grandma said again. ''E made sure you was in the will.'

I nodded thoughtfully. I had lost Grandpa but won the battle to go to art school. How to balance these two events? I did not like being compensated for grief by money. I dared not be too excited about going to art school, now, for fear of trivialising Grandpa's death. I hated the trite phrases trotted out by Grandma's cronies: 'Every cloud has a silver lining,' they would say. But Grandpa hadn't died so I could attend art school. Wouldn't I have found some way to study art anyway? Wouldn't I have preferred to have Grandpa alive? 'Win some, lose some,' the cronies would shrug. 'Easy come, easy go.' Was that how one formed a philosophy?

I had said nothing to anyone about Grandpa's death.

The official story was that he had died in his own bed, during the night. 'From natural causes,' Dr Kossoff had testified, and no doubt that was true, but Hilda and I knew that there had been more to it than that. I had not seen Hilda since that night. She stayed away from the funeral, even though she had every right to be there. I knew she wanted to avoid a scene and thought it tactful and kind of her, knowing how much she had loved Grandpa. I would visit her, I decided, right after leaving Grandma. But there was no reply to Hilda's bell when I rang it.

*

After submitting my application, I was interviewed by the Principal of St Martin's School of Art. I had imagined a Bohemian type in black beret, but he turned out to be tweedy and country-squire-ish, with ruddy cheeks and a brisk manner.

'Big chap like you!' He looked me up and down approvingly before taking a quick glance through my sketchbook. 'You should be able to look out for yourself in a place like Soho, eh?' He chuckled.

Look out for myself? I was on first-name terms with most of the prostitutes and pimps who made it such a wicked place! The girls wore my mother's cast-off clothing. I nodded. The Principal told me I could enter the Foundation Course the following September. Thanking him, I backed gratefully out of his presence, as if he were royalty. My height had decided my acceptance into art school, not my talent. But nobody needed to know.

*

And then the family suddenly fell apart as if Grandpa had been the steel pin holding everything in place. One night, some months after the funeral, Auntie Joyce burst into our house, red-eyed and hysterical, sobbing that Uncle Frankie had left her to move into the Paddington flat of an Irish barmaid.

Shortly after that, I arrived home from school one afternoon to find my father pacing the back lawn, repeating: 'Your mother's gone mad! Your mother's gone mad!'

I raced upstairs to their bedroom. Her empty wardrobe stood open, the jangling hangers and traces of *Femme* perfume telling me everything. Mum had gone! For a moment, I felt completely blank. I stood by the window where, at six or seven, I had waited hours for her dear head to appear at the foot of the hill, returning home with heavy shopping. I found Rachel in her bedroom, weeping over a letter Mum had left. She handed it to me.

> You're the best children in the world [it read]. Nobody has such lovely children as I've got. You know how much I love you all, how I've put you first for nineteen years. Now I have a chance for a new life, please don't hate me for taking it. We'll all be together again one day, I promise. Please remember – I'm not leaving *you*, I'm leaving your father. Your loving Mum. P.S. Please forgive me.

'*I* forgive her,' Rachel sobbed. 'I *do*. I don't blame anyone for not living with *him*.'

We went into my bedroom to watch Dad pacing the lawn, hiding behind the net curtains so he wouldn't see us. Rachel gave me a little pat and returned to her room. I reread the note Mum had left us. She had written an address after the P.S. I scribbled it down and went to look for Lawrence to break the news gently to him, but I couldn't find him.

My blankness slowly ebbed away to be replaced by something worse – the prospect of life with just Dad. Mum had been the only good thing about living at home. She had been the buffer, the interpreter, the smoother-over between us and Dad. She had always made everything all right. What on earth would we do without her? I needed to talk to her. She had never refused me anything; if I went to see her now, could I persuade her to come back? I glanced at my watch. It was half past five.

Saying nothing to anyone, I quickly left the house,

squeezing pyjamas and toothbrush into my satchel in case Mum asked me to spend the night. I looked up Devonshire Place in my *A to Z* and took the tube to Baker Street, walking down Marylebone Road. It was one of those grey, treeless streets between Madame Tussaud's and Harley Street. With a shock I found the number and saw that 'Flat A' was the basement. In my innocence, I had imagined basements were used only for coal storage or dustbins. Now my mother was living in one. I descended the twisting concrete steps and rang the bell. Perhaps the interior would be much better than the unprepossessing exterior? The door was opened with a flourish, by Vito. He broke into his usual dazzling smile, pumping my hand to cover his embarrassment, but I could see alarm in his wide pale blue eyes.

'Is my mother here?' I asked.

He didn't exactly welcome me in. 'Yes.' He nodded vigorously. 'Mummy is here but she is very tired. She sleeps.'

'I'd like to see her, please,' I said.

His smile glazed a little as he repeated, 'She sleeps.'

'Please,' I said. Whoever would have thought that I would be begging Vito to allow me access to my mother!

With a grudging shrug he stood aside and let me into the poky entrance hall. He led the way down a dark corridor and knocked on a door. A muffled 'Mmmm?' came from inside.

'Your son is here!' Vito called through the door.

'My son?' Mum opened the door, dressed in a robe. 'Darling.' She smiled wanly, reaching for me. 'How did you find me? Are you all right?'

I hugged her and we went into her room. It was cramped. There was really only space for a bed. Her suitcases were there and some of her clothes were heaped on a chair.

'I don't know what came over me,' she apologised. 'I suddenly felt so tired. I took a pill to calm me down, sometimes they make you sleepy.'

'You would like some tea?' Vito asked, and disappeared at my mother's nod.

I tried not to look around but the worn carpet and stained wallpaper were a shock. I had never seen Mum in less than spotless, bright surroundings, nor so ill at ease and nervous. She groped for her cigarettes and quickly lit up.

'Are the others all right?' she asked me. 'Rachel? Lawrence?'

'Rachel's crying,' I told her. 'I haven't seen Lawrence yet.'

'You won't tell them what this place is like, darling?' she begged.

'But – why did you take it?' I asked.

'It's Vito's flat,' she said. 'We'll find something better.'

'Something big enough for all of us?' I asked hopefully.

She avoided my eyes, taking a long drag of smoke. 'Well, we'll see,' she said.

'Come back, Mum,' I said.

Vito knocked on the door and entered with a tray of tea and biscuits, exactly like a waiter. He *was* a waiter, I remembered. He set it down carefully on her bed.

'Oh, thank you, Vito,' my mother said gratefully.

'Is nothing,' he snapped, and withdrew.

'We want you back,' I said again. Mum stirred sugar into her tea and sipped it, but I couldn't bring myself to drink mine.

'Look, darling.' She replaced the cup. 'I've thought very hard about this. I think I must stick to my guns. You must have realised things were not very good between your father and me.'

'You seemed all right,' I said. 'You love working.'

'Yes, but I didn't like plates being thrown at me or being called a prostitute in front of my children,' Mum smiled sadly.

'But we all hate him too. Why should we have to live with him?'

'He's your father,' she said. 'You can't hate him. He loves you and he'll see that you eat and have a roof over your heads. May will stay on, to cook and clean for you all. You'll manage without me.'

'We won't!' I cried.

She took both my hands, leaning forward. 'Darling, let me ask you something.' Her brown eyes searched mine, pleadingly. 'Do you want me back even if I'd be unhappy?'

'Yes!' I blurted out.

'Well, that's very selfish of you, darling.' She stubbed out her cigarette and placed the tray on the floor. Then she took a huge breath, regaining her vigour. 'But I'm glad I brought up my children to be selfish,' she claimed. 'You'll be much happier that way. Unselfish people get a lousy deal. I've put you all first for nineteen years, now *I'm* going to be selfish. It's my turn to be happy.' I stared at her as she lay down on the bed. She didn't look at all happy. She looked strained and tired and … unhappy. I knew, with all the wisdom of my fifteen years, that Vito wasn't going to make her happy.

'Will you marry him?' I asked.

She turned from my stare. 'We'll see,' she said quietly.

There was another knock on the door. Vito opened it, unsmiling for a change. 'You must let Mummy rest,' he said to me. 'She's very tired.'

I glanced angrily at him, outraged that he thought he could tell me what to do. I bit back an angry comment. Instead, I looked at Mum. And all my resolve collapsed. She wanted me to leave too. I was in the way, spoiling her adventure. This new, unpleasant, unwanted feeling made me lean over to kiss her goodbye. There was no question of staying the night. I couldn't wait to get out of there.

Walking towards the Tube station, blinded by tears, I was furious at myself. On the train home, I told myself that I could no longer be a little boy who needed his Mummy. Growing up was not a gradual process at all, I realised. It was a short painful moment when you progressed to a new level – a growing-up moment. But – God – how many of these moments would I have to endure?

*

We became the neighbourhood celebrities – the children whose mother, after learning to drive, had run off with a

young Italian waiter. Friends' mothers baked us cakes and
came to console Dad.

'Get it off your chest,' they advised him, settling down
to a cup of tea with him in the kitchen.

And Dad suddenly had a lot to say, playing the part
of aggrieved husband. Although we quite enjoyed the
notoriety and the home-baked cakes, it was upsetting to
hear Mum criticised by people who hardly knew her and
knew even less about her marriage or what a wonderful
mother she had been. Dad was on the phone to
Grandma nightly, complaining as if he had been sold
faulty goods. Grandma, speechless at her daughter's
wickedness, tended to agree with him. She invited us to
dinners and spent the meal clucking her tongue at us,
crying, 'Your mother's living with a *yock*! A *yock* she's
living with!'

Once Dad had finally accepted that Mum was not about
to return, he replaced all the lightbulbs in the house with
forty-watt bulbs, without telling us. For a time, we thought
we were going blind, until we discovered why reading had
become so difficult. Mum was the kind of woman who lit
up rooms when she entered them, so the house now
seemed doubly dark. Dad also ripped out all the telephone
extensions, unplugged the fridge (from then on it was used
as a cupboard), turned down the heating thermostat, sold
his car and travelled to work by bus. Grief affects people in
different ways.

*

My childhood was over. From now on I would have to look
out for myself.

'Your whole life is ahead of you,' grown-ups liked to
say. But what kind of life? I would be the youngest (but
tallest) student at St Martin's School of Art, 'drawing from
the clothed and unclothed model'. That would surely be a
lot more exciting than drawing the back of Lawrence's
head. I knew that the solution to my collapsing family life
was to throw myself into my work. Only by realising my

ambition to be a good artist, perhaps a great one, could I make sense of life.

*

Mum moved to a larger flat in the same area. At least it wasn't a basement, but there were only two bedrooms. She was planning to open her longed-for sandwich shop. She inherited some money from Grandpa and expected a financial settlement from Dad in due course. Vito immediately left Ciao, of course, to manage a rival Italian restaurant. He was devoutly Catholic, and Mum said he felt too guilty at breaking up a home to face us. That was fine with us. We always asked when we would all be living together again, and she always promised: 'Soon, soon, I just have to work things out –' but weeks, then months, passed and we had to face the fact that it simply wasn't going to happen. We were stuck with Dad. We weren't all going to live together again, after all.

*

After the requisite year's mourning, Grandma's cronies attempted to find her a new husband. She enjoyed the courting part, the dinners and the gifts, but she had no real intention of remarrying. Richer than her sons' wildest dreams (she now owned fifty per cent of their business), Grandma never moved from the Edgware Road flat and drove her local bank manager crazy by demanding to see her savings, in cash, each year. The bank had to send out for supplies of banknotes, count them out for her and watch her shove the bundles of notes back under the grille. She just wanted to see her money.

Mary moved into Uncle Jack's old room, my uncles allowing Grandma to believe that she still paid Mary her original wage of £10 a week ('All she's worth,' Grandma maintained), secretly topping it up with a further £250 to stop her from leaving. Thanks to Mary's care and their daily, shared bottle of Scotch, Grandma survived into her nineties.

*

My father eventually married a respectable Jewish widow and shared her cosy St John's Wood flat where he was unexpectedly happy for the rest of his life. His second wife had the knack of laughing him out of his bad humour. Win some, lose some. The most surprising characters won, the most deserving sometimes lost. Dad was invited to Grandma's Friday dinners along with his new wife. So were Frankie and his new Irish wife, with whom he had a son. Joyce, banished from the magic kingdom, returned to America with her children. Vito was not presented to Grandma and after a while my mother lost contact with her. The brothers were forbidden to see their sister. Easy come, easy go.

*

Mum finally opened her sandwich shop, where one of the many fillings on offer was banana with chocolate flakes. It was not very popular. Her volatile affair with Vito lasted twelve years, leaving her disillusioned and hopeless when he left. She sought solace in a series of desperate relationships. Shunned by her family, drinking, smoking, loving too much, my beautiful mother burned out in a bright, self-destructive flame.

*

I was considered a bit of a hermit by my family in later life. I blamed my overload of work (I designed posters, book covers, record albums), but actually I did not feel comfortable around them and limited my exposure to engagements, barmitzvahs, and weddings. I stopped visiting Grandma when her drunken insults became too frequent. The decent people around her melted away, leaving a core of hangers-on who enjoyed her lavish meals and unlimited Scotch and were prepared to laugh off her insults. My uncles opened steak-houses, ice-cream parlours and hotels, and walked past me on the street looking the other way, surrounded by an entourage of yes-men. Frankie gained weight, had heart problems, and eventually died in middle-age. Jack and Christine enjoyed a long marriage, producing four children I never met. We lost our Mum far too early: Dad lived well into his eighties.

*

The events of my adolescence are etched upon my unwanted photographic plate of a memory, as if part of my consciousness is stuck there. I have never really felt grown-up, but for an artist that can be a good thing. On Friday nights, the aroma of Grandpa's cigar still wafts up to my bedroom as I try to sleep, while downstairs the grown-ups play poker and scheme to make a better living.

When I was twelve, I believed that every boy had a family like mine. I thought every boy had a beautiful mother who adored him, a bad-tempered father who frightened him and a Grandma with bright orange hair, white face and ruby talons. By the time I reached fifteen, I was pretty sure that no one had a family quite like mine.

As for being Jewish, by rights I should think it's 'a lot of baloney', as my father maintained, but I have tried to learn a little more about my religion. Through the friendship of an elegant old Viennese lady, through reading Isaac Bashevis Singer, through various conversations, I glimpsed some of the compassion, philosophy and spirituality I had missed out on the first time around. I may never have faith but I will always be a Jew. 'You *think* Jewish,' Grandma liked to say, and there *is* a Jewish attitude to life, bound up with humour. I like to think it's the ability to laugh at oneself. And at life, too, sometimes.

Two lovable Polish cousins, Cecia and Joe, a married couple who lived in Connecticut and who had lost twin daughters in the Holocaust, used to visit London annually. They were from my father's side of the family and had blue concentration-camp numbers tattooed on their forearms. If one of them hoisted a sleeve or shrugged off a cardigan, all conversation suddenly stopped. We would stare at the tattoos, not daring to ask about them. We knew they were the scars of something terrible, something unspeakable. And because it was unspeakable, we never heard their story. Perhaps we should have? There would have been tears, pain, but at least we would have known, having heard it from their own mouths.

Each time a family member died, we lost precious clues as to the kind of Jews we were. Bad Jews, surely, for no one was very observant, but bad Jews are Jews, too. How I regret not having questioned my grandparents more closely about their birthplaces, their childhoods, the dates and our history. Perhaps I am equally to blame for the lack of family history, for I never told my mother what Grandma confessed in the basement of her flat. I didn't see the point. Would it have made her any happier? Logic, or intuition, said not. After thinking it over, I kept the information to myself, rather proud to be the custodian of my family's secrets.

DUCKBACKS

Diary of a Man in Despair
Friedrich Reck-Malleczewen   £6.99 Paperback   0 7156 3100 4

A forgotten literary masterpiece by a Prussian aristocrat whose fascinating journal and indictment of Hitler's regime, written between 1936 and 1944, has astonished and delighted readers and critics alike.

'I beg you to read this bitterly courageous book'
Frederic Raphael, *The Sunday Times*

Cleopatra's Wedding Present
Travels through Syria
Robert Tewdwr Moss   £6.99 Paperback   0 7156 3099 7

Robert Tewdwr Moss describes his travel experiences with rare charm and aplomb.

'it would be hard to find a more archly entertaining, slyly informative, or poignant travel book than this'
Philip Hoare, *Independent*

The Way of Hermes
Translated by Clement Salaman, Dorine van Oyen, William D. Wharton, Jean-Pierre Mahé   £6.99 Paperback   0 7156 3093 8

The *Corpus Hermeticum* is a collection of short philosophical treatises, a powerful fusion of Greek and Egyptian thought, written in Greek in Alexandria between the first and third centuries AD. They are still read as inspirational spiritual writings today.

These translations of Hermetic writings and aphorisms provide both general reader and scholar with new English versions, based on reliable texts and faithful to the spirit and beauty of the original.

One Woman's War
Eve-Ann Prentice   £6.99 Paperback   0 7156 3104 7

A personal account of the war in the Balkans by a senior *Times* journalist, hailed by Harold Pinter as `a powerful and important book'.

'*One Woman's War*, spurred by the death of the author's Serb interpreter during the Nato bombing of Kosovo, is an unself-conscious, intensely human and exceptionally honest reflection of the past ten years of conflict'

Allan Mallinson, *The Times*

The Pig: A British History
Julian Wiseman   £6.99 Paperback   0 7156 3092 X

A history of one of Britain's best-loved creatures, including the development of its husbandry.

'elegantly slender ¼ full of delightful pictures of the different breeds. Gripping'

Independent

The Captain
The Life and Times of Simon Raven
Michael Barber   £6.99 Paperback   0 7156 3138 1

With an updated prologue, this tremendously well-received biography of the late Simon Raven, one of Britain's most idio-syncratic and talented characters, is published for the first time in mass market paperback.

this biography is a minor masterpiece'   *Evening Standard*

On Beauty and Being Just
Elaine Scarry   £6.99 Paperback   0 7156 3134 9

An inspirational and extremely lucid philosophical critique on the interpretation of beauty.

'a lucid, passionate and cultivated book'   *The Tablet*

Horace: A Life

Peter Levi   £6.99 Paperback   0 7156 3136 5

The first comprehensive biography for 40 years of the life of the great Roman poet.

'a fine example of an old-fashioned literary form: the book by well-informed and enthusiastic amateur, talking to the reader about a poet he has loved for many years'   *The Spectator*

The Uncollected Dorothy Parker

Edited by Stuart Y Silverstein   £6.99 Pbk   0 7156 2937 9

122 forgotten pieces displaying the raw talent and dexterity of America's most renowned cynic. Here is the distinctive wit, irony and precision that continues to attract succeeding generations of writers.

'this volume is a great event'   *Daily Mail*

A Short Walk Down Fleet Street
From Beaverbrook to Boycott

Alan Watkins   £6.99 Paperback   0 7156 3143 8

'entertaining and enlightening … Watkins plays Aubrey to the many remarkable personalities who populated old Fleet Street, defining this lost world through a series of splendid pen portraits'   *Sunday Telegraph*

'The Law is a Ass'
An Illustrated Anthology of Legal Quotations

Compiled & Edited by Ronald Irving £6.99 Pbk 0 7156 3142 X

This entertaining compendium contains many witty, cynical and sometimes profound observations, sayings and anecdotes about the law, lawyers, courts, justice, crime and punishment, libel and wills.

An Intelligent Person's Guide to Ethics

Mary Warnock   £6.99 Paperback   0 7156 3089 X

'one of the best guides to ethics available'

Ray Monk, *Sunday Telegraph*

'this admirable book fully lives up to its title'

Robert Grant, *The Times*

An Intelligent Person's Guide to History

John Vincent   £6.99 Paperback   0 7156 3090 3

'not only is Vincent one of the great historians of 19th-century British politics, he is also that rarest of things in academic history: a witty prose stylist'

Niall Ferguson, *Daily Telegraph*

An Intelligent Person's Guide to Dickens

Michael Slater   £6.99 Paperback   0 7156 3088 1

'Michael Slater has an encyclopaedic knowledge of Dickens's writings'   *Times Literary Supplement*

An Intelligent Person's Guide to Modern Ireland

John Waters   £6.99 Paperback   0 7156 3091 1

'John Waters skilfully attacks those who decry any sense of nationalism or belittle any aspiration that the two parts of Ireland should be united'

Michael O'Toole, *Irish News* (Belfast)

Boogie-Woogie

Danny Moynihan   £5.99 Paperback   0 7156 3102 0

Much-praised hilarious satire of the incestuous world of New York's contemporary art scene.

'Moynihan's first novel is spectacular stuff'

Harriet Lane, *Observer*

Intimate Cartographies

Lynne Alexander   £5.99 Paperback   0 7156 3095 4

A beautifully-constructed tale of a mapmaker who comes to terms with loss through the discipline of her work.

'Alexander has chosen the most difficult of subjects, the death of a child. She has treated it with sensitivity and wit, manic levity and the utmost respect, and has created something quite haunting'

Carol Birch, *Independent*

Too Fast To Live

Bidisha   £5.99 Paperback   0 7156 3098 9

A modern-day story of misdirected passions and amoral ambitions in a subversive rewriting of the Arthurian saga.

'Bidisha is clearly a dazzlingly creative writer'

Anthea Lawson, *The Times*

Charlotte
The Final Journey of Jane Eyre

D.M. Thomas   £5.99 Paperback   0 7156 3094 6

An extraordinary, imaginative deconstruction of Charlotte Brontë's *Jane Eyre*, set partly in modern-day Martinique.

'a wickedly irreverent antidote to earnest study'

Charlotte Cory, *Independent*

Never Trust A Rabbit

Jeremy Dyson   £5.99 Paperback   0 7156 3097 0

Twelve enchantingly surreal stories, recently serialised on BBC Radio Four, by Jeremy Dyson, one of *The League of Gentlemen*.

a stunning debut. His stories nestle in the little chink between Roald Dahl and Borges'

Adam Mars-Jones, *The Observer*

Layer Cake

J.J. Connolly   £5.99 Paperback   0 7156 3096 2

The critically-acclaimed contemporary gangland thriller set in London's underworld, described by Bruce Reynolds as 'the best crime novel I've ever read'.

'*Layer Cake* is a storming piece of work, funny and serious by turns with an abiding sense of conviction'   *Guardian*

The Lantern Bearers

Ronald Frame   £5.99 Paperback   0 7156 3133 0

WINNER OF THE 2000 SALTIRE BOOK OF THE YEAR AWARD, SCOTLAND'S MOST PRESTIGIOUS LITERARY PRIZE.

As the biographer of a dead composer of the 1960s Neil Pritchard is forced to make a moral decision which risks exposing his involvement in the violent events that took place 35 years earlier on the remote Solway Firth, when he was the composer's final muse.

'exceedingly powerful, laced with impending menace from the opening page'   *Scotland on Sunday*

Valentine's Day
Women Against Men: Stories of Revenge

Edited by Alice Thomas Ellis   £5.99 Paperback   0 7156 3140 3

A brilliant collection of revenge stories by some of the finest contemporary women writers around.

'a sharp anthology, both clever and pointed'   *The Times*

'this cracking collection of Valentine's Day short stories does not mess around with the soppy stuff. This is a book not about romance, but revenge'   *Daily Mail*

'a fiery and fun mix which is deeply satisfying to read'

     Amazon.co.uk

A Kind of Warfare
Portrait of a Serial Seducer
Deborah Bosley   £5.99 Paperback   0 7156 3139 X

A frontline account of the battle of the sexes in which an `Alfie' for our times is hopelessly addicted to serial seduction and romantic self-absorption, until love hits him and he is hoist by his own petard.

'Deborah Bosley's great achievement is to tread a clear and confident path between the surging purple of her subject matter and the economical, self-deprecating wit with which she writes about it'

Literary Review

The Best of Oscar Wilde
Edited by Robert Pearce   £5.99 Paperback   0 7156 3149 7

Oscar Wilde is one of the most quotable of authors, as this collection of extracts from his prose clearly demonstrates. It also illustrates the full breadth, from the delightfully comic to the profoundly serious, of this supremely talented but ultimately tragic figure.

Lads: Love poetry of the trenches
Edited by Martin Taylor   £6.99 Paperback   0 7156 3145 4

A remarkable anthology of many largely unknown poems from the trenches, which illustrates the extraordinary range of emotions generated by the horror of the First World War and the experience of trench warfare.

'a model of tactful evocation and historical sensibility'

Andrew Motion, *Observer*

Poetic Gems

Introduction by Billy Connolly
William McGonagall   £6.99 Paperback   0 7156 3151 9

William McGonagall, known as the Greatest Bad Verse Writer of his age, was unrecognised during his lifetime but now has admirers all over the world ... including Billy Connolly, who has written an affectionate introduction to the anthology.

'even a dour literary world such as 19th century Scotland needs its own Don Quixote, and McGonagall fitted the bill'

Yorkshire Post

Reach for the Ground: The downhill struggle of Jeffrey Bernard

Foreword by Peter O'Toole
Jeffrey Bernard   £6.99 Paperback   0 7156 3150 0

An irresistible collection of the best of Jeffrey Bernard's **Low Life** columns for the Spectator, including an affectionate introduction by Peter O'Toole and three sparkling autobiographical essays.

'howlingly funny, plaintive as an oboe and as smart as a butcher's knife'

Daily Express

'no one tells an anecdote better, no matter how apocryphal it is. ... he is our Boswell, our Pepys. Give him a large one'

The Scotsman

The Dream Dictionary for the Modern Dreamer

Tim Etchells   £6.99 Paperback   0 7156 3154 3

A mischievous glimpse into the contemporary subconscious and a playful, irreverent portrait of 21st century life.

'the perfect work for fragmented, poorly understood lives'
Nicholas Lezard, *Guardian*

A Memoir: People & Places

Mary Warnock   £6.99 Paperback   0 7156 3141 1

In an intelligent and engaging memoir, philosopher Mary Warnock reflects on some of the people who have influenced or intrigued her throughout her career, offering a highly personal view of an important period in 20th century history.

'one of the best and most civilised reads of the year'

Financial Times

'anyone who wants to know how twentieth-century Britain worked should read this memoir'

Jessica Mann, *Literary Review*

The Undiscovered Chekhov: Fifty-One New Stories

Translated by Peter Constantine   £6.99 Pbk   0 7156 3155 1

Peter Constantine's award?winning translation of these vivid stories was published to great acclaim, and casts new light on the development of the great playwright's development into a literary genius.

'glittering splinters of genius'

John Bayley, *The Spectator*

'a sparkling translation'

George Steiner, *Observer*

The Comedy Man

D.J. Taylor   £5.99 Paperback   0 7156 3157 8

D.J. Taylor's vivid evocation of post-war English life tells the story of Ted King, the 'straight' half of a comedy duo that rose to fame in the late 70s; ranging in time and place from rainswept Norfolk seafronts in the 50s to 60s Soho clubland, from bombs exploding in Cyprus to Oswald Mosley's Daimler coursing through the East End.

'Taylor is utterly enthralling in memoir mode … a rhapsody'

Bob Monkhouse, *Guardian*

The Handsomest Sons in the World!

Harold Carlton   £5.99 Paperback   0 7156 3158 6

An autobiographical romp through north-west London and Soho in the 50s in which thirteen-year-old Howard struggles to understand himself and his family, with the help of Freud and his knowledgeable elder sister Rachel.

'a remarkable achievement'

John Carey, *The Sunday Times*

'a pleasure to read ¼ an unsentimental book, neither a whine nor a boast, about growing up in a difficult family'

Salley Vickers

SIEGFRIED SASSOON Volume I: The Making of a War Poet

Jean Moorcroft Wilson   £8.99 Paperback   0 7956 3121 7

The first volume of Moorcroft Wilson's critically acclaimed biography of one of the twentieth century's finest poets, covering Sassoon's life from his birth in 1886 until the end of the Great War. Published to coincide with Volume II in hardback.

'a story in which the roots are as interesting as the core ¼ invaluable to historians of the period'

Andrew Motion, *The Times*

'a compelling tale'

Sunday Telegraph

ORDER FORM (BLOCK CAPITALS PLEASE)

SURNAME _____ FIRST NAME _____

ADDRESS _____

_____

_____ POSTCODE _____

METHOD OF PAYMENT (PLEASE TICK AS APPROPRIATE)

☐ Invoice to my Grantham Book Services account
☐ By cheque (payable to Duckworth Publishers)
☐ Please send account opening details (trade customers only)
☐ By credit card (Access/ Visa / Mastercard / Amex)

Card no: ☐☐☐☐☐☐☐☐☐☐☐☐☐☐☐☐☐☐☐

Expiry date: __/__/__ Authorising Signature: _____

POSTAGE (Private customers) Please note that the following postage and packing charges should be added to your order:

UK deliveries: £3 on orders up to £16; £4 on orders over £16
Export surface: £3.50 for first book + £0.50 for each additional book
Export airmail: £7 for the first book + £2 for each additional book

QTY	ISBN	TITLE	PRICE	TOTAL
____	_____	_____	_____	_____
____	_____	_____	_____	_____
____	_____	_____	_____	_____
____	_____	_____	_____	_____
____	_____	_____	_____	_____
____	_____	_____	_____	_____
____	_____	_____	_____	_____

TOTAL £ _____

To: Sales Dept, Duckworth, 61 Frith Street, London W1D 3JL
Tel:+44 (0) 20 7434 4242 Fax: +44 (0) 20 7434 4420
Heidi@duckworth-publishers.co.uk